WeightWatchers®

W9-BBQ-266

Most Recipes Featuring Weight Watchers® Products

SENSIBLY TASTY

deliciously easy

50 Anytime, Anywhere Recipes

WILEY

Wiley Publishing, Inc.

Weight Watchers International, Inc.

EDITORIAL DIRECTOR
Hugh Dever

CREATIVE DIRECTOR
Claudia Dal Lago

NUTRITION CONSULTANT
Jessica Smerling, R.D., C.D.N.

RECIPE DEVELOPER
Elizabeth Fassberg, M.P.H., R.D., C.D.N.

PHOTOGRAPHY
Tina Rupp

FOOD STYLING
Megan Fawn Schlow

PROP STYLING
Cathy Cook

Wiley Publishing, Inc.

PUBLISHER
Natalie Chapman

EXECUTIVE EDITOR
Anne Ficklen

SENIOR EDITORIAL ASSISTANT
Charleen Barila

ART DIRECTOR
Tai Blanche

MANUFACTURING MANAGER
Kevin Watt

For general information on our other products and services or to obtain technical support please contact our Customer Care Department within the U.S. at 800-762-2974, outside the U.S. at 317-572-3993 or fax 317-572-4002.

Wiley also publishes its books in a variety of electronic formats. Some content that appears in print may not be available in electronic books. For more information about Wiley products, visit our web site at www.wiley.com.

ISBN: 978-0-470-25689-3 (pbk.)

Manufactured in the United States of America

10 9 8 7 6 5 4 3 2 1

Cover photos: Grown-up Creamsicles with White Wine and Fresh Mint (page 91), Turkey-Bagel Sandwich with Avocado and Green Apple (page 40), Breakfast Veggie Casserole (page 24)

A Word About Weight Watchers

Weight Watchers teaches you how to live a healthy lifestyle so you learn how to lose weight and keep it off.

Since 1963, Weight Watchers has grown from a handful of people to millions of enrollments annually. Today, Weight Watchers is recognized as the leading name in safe and sensible weight control. Weight Watchers members form diverse groups, from youths to senior citizens, attending meetings virtually around the globe. Weight-loss and weight-management results vary by individual, but we recommend that you attend Weight Watchers meetings to benefit from the supportive environment you'll find there and follow the comprehensive Weight Watchers program which includes food plans, an activity plan, and a thinking skills plan. And we offer certain foods to expand your choice and help you along your weight management journey. These foods provide a convenient way to save calories without sacrificing great taste.

Keep in mind you don't have to buy the Weight Watchers products in order to be successful with the Weight Watchers program. However, many members tell us that the Weight Watchers name on food products is extremely useful in helping them follow the Program.

For the Weight Watchers meeting nearest you, call 800-START NOW. For information on bringing Weight Watchers to your workplace, call 800-8AT-WORK. Also, visit us at our Web site, **www.WeightWatchers.com**, or look for Weight Watchers Magazine at your newsstand or in your meeting rooms.

FREE WEIGHT WATCHERS NEWSLETTER!
SIGN UP TODAY!

It's easy! Simply visit WeightWatchers.com/newsletter to sign up. Each week, you'll get:

Delicious recipes · Success stories · Weight-loss tips

To learn more about how Weight Watchers can help you, call 1 (800) 410-1199.

ABOUT OUR RECIPES

We make every effort to ensure that you will have success with our recipes. For best results and for nutritional accuracy, please keep the following guidelines in mind:

- Recipes in this book have been developed to help you along your weight management journey and maintain a healthier lifestyle.

- Many recipes use Weght Watchers sensible food products in the ingredients. These great-tasting products can be found at your local supermarket, and are an easy, convenient option to help you stay on track throughout the day. Go to **www.WeightWatchers.com/sensiblefoods** for more information.

- We include **POINTS**® values so that you can use any of the recipes if you are following the Weight Watchers® program. **POINTS** values are assigned based on calories, fat (grams), and fiber (grams) provided for a serving size of a recipe.

- Vegetarian recipes are marked to help you identify meatless options easily.

- All recipes feature approximate nutritional information; Our recipes are analyzed for Calories (Cal), Total Fat (Fat), Saturated Fat (Sat Fat), Trans Fat (Trans Fat), Cholesterol (Chol), Sodium (Sod), Carbohydrates (Carb), Dietary Fiber (Fib), Protein (Prot), and Calcium (Calc).

- Nutritional information for recipes that include meat, poultry, and fish are based on cooked skinless, boneless portions (unless otherwise stated), with the fat trimmed.

- We recommend that you buy lean meat and poultry, then trim it of all visible fat before cooking. When poultry is cooked with the skin on, we suggest removing the skin before eating.

- It is implied that all fresh fruits, vegetables, and greens in recipes should be rinsed before using.

- Any substitutions made to the ingredients will alter the "Per serving" nutritional information and may affect the **POINTS** value.

- We have provided numerous tips, health notes, and food facts to offer additional suggestions on how to enhance the recipes and incorporate them into your everyday lifestyle.

- If tips suggest to add additional ingredients, please note the **POINTS** value of the recipe changes. To determine an accurate **POINTS** value, we recommend you register on **www.WeightWatchers.com** and use the **POINTS** calculator.

DRY AND LIQUID MEASUREMENT EQUIVALENTS

Use the following chart as a handy guide for all our recipes.

Teaspoons	Tablespoons	Cups	Fluid Ounces
3 teaspoons	1 tablespoon		½ fluid ounce
6 teaspoons	2 tablespoons	⅛ cup	1 fluid ounce
8 teaspoons	2 tablespoons plus 2 teaspoons	⅙ cup	
12 teaspoons	4 tablespoons	¼ cup	2 fluid ounces
15 teaspoons	5 tablespoons	⅓ cup minus 1 teaspoon	
16 teaspoons	5 tablespoons plus 1 teaspoon	⅓ cup	
18 teaspoons	6 tablespoons	¼ cup plus 2 tablespoons	3 fluid ounces
24 teaspoons	8 tablespoons	½ cup	4 fluid ounces
30 teaspoons	10 tablespoons	½ cup plus 2 tablespoons	5 fluid ounces
32 teaspoons	10 tablespoons plus 2 teaspoons	⅔ cup	
36 teaspoons	12 tablespoons	¾ cup	6 fluid ounces
42 teaspoons	14 tablespoons	1 cup minus 2 tablespoons	7 fluid ounces
45 teaspoons	15 tablespoons	1 cup minus 1 tablespoon	
48 teaspoons	16 tablespoons	1 cup	8 fluid ounces

Note: Measurement of less than ⅛ teaspoon is considered a dash or a pinch.

1

Simple
Breakfasts

Toasted Blueberry Muffin
with Warm Citrus Compote **8**

CONTENTS >>

2

Take It
with You

28 Lentil Salad with Fresh Mint
and Goat Cheese

3

Dinner for One

Pan-Seared Salmon with
Basil-Dijon Cream Sauce 68

4

Casual Entertaining

70 Lemon-Raspberry Bread Pudding

1

Individual Ham, Cheese,
and Veggie Frittatas, page 27

SIMPLE
breakfasts

10   Make-Ahead Breakfast Fig Spread

12   Bagel Spread with Smoked Salmon and Dill Cream Cheese

14   Toasted Blueberry Muffin with Warm Citrus Compote

16   Warm Chocolate Muffins with Baked Peaches and Sour Cream

18   Cornmeal Pancakes with Fruity Yogurt Sauce

19   Baked Blueberry-Peach French Toast

20   Orange-Banana Yogurt Chiller

22   Eggs Florentine

24   Breakfast Veggie Casserole

26   Breakfast Pizza with Turkey Sausage

27   Individual Ham, Cheese, and Veggie Frittatas

MAKE-AHEAD BREAKFAST FIG SPREAD

6 ounces dried Black Mission figs, stems removed

1 teaspoon fresh ginger, diced

> **1 cup Tropicana Light 'n Healthy Orange Juice Beverage**

1½ teaspoons lemon juice

pinch salt

Hands-On Prep 5 minutes	
Cook 25 minutes	
Serves 6 (2 tablespoons per serving)	
Makes ¾ cup spread	

1 Combine all ingredients in medium saucepan and bring to a boil. Reduce heat to medium-low and simmer, stirring occasionally until liquid has evaporated by ¾, about 15 minutes. Remove from heat.

2 Place all ingredients in food processor and pulse on medium-high speed until mixture is well combined and smooth.

Per serving (2 tablespoons): 80 Cal, 0 g Fat, 0 g Trans Fat, 0 mg Chol, 25 mg Sod, 20 g Carb, 3 g Fib, 1 g Prot, 8% Calc. **POINTS** value (spread only): **1**.

good idea Are your mornings too hectic for prepping breakfast recipes? This versatile spread can be prepared a day or two ahead of time, and stored in an airtight container in the refrigerator.

Try spreading it on toasted Weight Watchers Wheat English Muffins with 1 tablespoon of Weight Watchers Reduced Fat Whipped Cream Cheese Spread. Or, spice up a basic cheese-and-cracker plate when entertaining by adding a small bowl of fig spread.

BAGEL SPREAD WITH SMOKED SALMON AND DILL CREAM CHEESE

2 tablespoons Weight Watchers Reduced Fat Cream Cheese Spread

1½ teaspoons dill, finely chopped

¼ teaspoon lemon juice

1 ounce smoked or cured salmon, thinly sliced

1 Weight Watchers Bagel, split and toasted

Hands-On Prep 10 minutes

Serves 2

Makes 2 tablespoons

2 POINTS VALUE

1 Combine cream cheese, dill, and lemon juice in small mixing bowl. Mix well until all ingredients are fully incorporated.

2 Spread cream cheese mixture on both halves of bagel. Top each half with ½ ounce smoked salmon.

Per serving (½ bagel): 120 Cal, 3.5 g Fat, 0 g Trans Fat, 10 mg Chol, 330 mg Sod, 18 g Carb, 6 g Fib, 8 g Prot, 6% Calc. **POINTS** value: **2.**

good idea This recipe also works well at brunch parties. Serve the bagel spread with a fresh fruit platter and delicious mimosas. (To make mimosas, combine Tropicana Light 'n Healthy Orange Juice Beverage with your favorite champagne or sparkling wine in a champagne flute.)

TOASTED BLUEBERRY MUFFIN WITH WARM CITRUS COMPOTE

1 tablespoon cornstarch

1 teaspoon Splenda® Brown Sugar Blend

2 tablespoons water

½ cup Tropicana Light 'n Healthy Orange Juice Beverage

1 cup orange segments, divided

⅛ teaspoon pure vanilla extract

⅛ teaspoon lemon zest

⅛ teaspoon lime zest

3 Weight Watchers Blueberry Muffins (1 box)

Hands-On Prep 10 minutes

Cook 8 to 10 minutes (allow 10 additional minutes for cooling)

Serves 6

Makes ¾ cup of compote (2 tablespoons per muffin half)

2 POINTS VALUE

1 Preheat oven to 350°F.

2 In a medium saucepan, whisk together cornstarch, Splenda Brown Sugar Blend, and water. Whisk in orange juice beverage. While whisking constantly, bring mixture to a boil over medium heat, about 2 minutes. (This will thicken quickly, so make sure to whisk constantly to prevent lumps.)

3 Whisk in ½ cup orange segments and continue to simmer over medium-low heat for 6 to 8 minutes, stirring often. Orange segments should break down and sauce should thicken, but should not become stiff.

4 Remove sauce from heat. Stir in vanilla extract, lemon zest, and lime zest. Let cool for about 10 minutes.

5 While sauce is cooling, slice each muffin in half and lightly toast in the oven on both sides. Serve each person a muffin half topped with 2 tablespoons of compote. Garnish with remaining ½ cup orange segments.

Per serving (½ muffin): 120 Cal, 1.5 g Fat, 0 g Trans Fat, 10 mg Chol, 0 mg Sod, 27 g Carb, 2 g Fib, 2 g Prot, 2% Calc. **POINTS** value: **2.**

good idea Leftover compote can also be used as a delicious breakfast marmalade. Spread on whole-wheat toast or apple slices, or mix into fat-free plain yogurt. Refrigerate in an airtight container for up to 3 days.

SENSIBLE

deliciousness

Muffins Always on the go? The daily rush doesn't mean you can't make smart choices. Don't dash out the door without Weight Watchers Muffins in your bag!

These individually wrapped muffins come in four different flavors and are a delicious and smart way to start your day. Weight Watchers Muffins are an easy way to stay on track and make sensible choices throughout the day; whether you're craving a fruity breakfast or a chocolate midday snack, these muffins are sure to keep you satisfied. Each muffin has 0 grams of trans fat and is a good source of fiber.

Blueberry, Double Chocolate—only 3 ***POINTS*** value each!

TASTY SUGGESTIONS
Add a tasty topping to your favorite Weight Watchers Muffin for a delectable breakfast treat, like the Warm Chocolate Muffins with Baked Peaches and Sour Cream on page 16.

WARM CHOCOLATE MUFFINS WITH BAKED PEACHES AND SOUR CREAM

1 large ripe peach, halved and pitted
4 teaspoons Tropicana Light 'n Healthy Orange Juice Beverage
3 tablespoons reduced-fat sour cream
1 Weight Watchers Double Chocolate Muffin, halved

Hands-On Prep 10 minutes

Cook 30 minutes

Serves 2

Makes 2 muffin halves

3 POINTS VALUE

1 Preheat oven to 400°F. Line 2 small baking sheets with parchment paper or aluminum foil and set aside.

2 Place peach halves cut side up onto baking sheet and lightly brush each half with 1 teaspoon orange juice beverage. Bake until peach halves reach desired softness, 20–30 minutes. Remove promptly and set aside to cool slightly. Once cooled cut into thin slices.

3 Meanwhile, combine sour cream and remaining orange juice beverage in a small bowl. Mix well until fully incorporated and set aside.

4 Warm muffin halves in oven for 2–3 minutes and remove promptly. Serve each muffin half with half of the baked peach slices and equal amounts sweetened sour cream.

Per serving (½ muffin): 160 Cal, 5 g Fat, 2.5 g Sat Fat, 0 g Trans Fat, 20 mg Chol, 190 mg Sod, 27 g Carb, 4 g Fib, 3 g Prot, 8% Calc. **POINTS** value: **3**.

good idea Boost the texture and nutritional value of this dish by adding a couple of teaspoons of chopped almonds or walnuts. This simple breakfast recipe also works well as a cozy dessert.

CORNMEAL PANCAKES WITH FRUITY YOGURT SAUCE

> **½ cup Tropicana Light 'n Healthy Orange Juice Beverage**

1 teaspoon cornstarch

1 cup frozen blueberries

¼ cup all-purpose flour

¼ teaspoon baking soda

½ teaspoon baking powder

⅛ teaspoon salt

¼ cup yellow cornmeal

1 teaspoon sugar

1 large egg white

½ cup reduced-fat buttermilk

> **¼ cup Weight Watchers Strawberry Yogurt (or flavor of choice)**

Hands-On Prep	15 minutes
Cook	15 minutes
Serves	2
Makes	4 pancakes, ⅔ cup sauce

4 POINTS VALUE

1 Whisk together orange juice beverage and cornstarch in a medium saucepan; add blueberries and bring to a boil on high heat. Continue cooking, stirring occasionally, until mixture has thickened, 3–5 minutes. Remove from heat and set aside to cool.

2 Combine flour, baking soda, baking powder, salt, cornmeal, and sugar in a medium bowl. Add egg white and buttermilk. Mix until just combined and set aside.

3 Heat a large nonstick sauté pan over medium heat and lightly coat with nonstick spray. Pour ¼ cup pancake batter onto hot surface. Repeat, making sure there is enough room in the pan to flip pancakes. Cook until tiny bubbles start to appear. Using a large spatula, flip pancakes and continue cooking until done, about 1 minute. Transfer pancakes to plate. Repeat with remaining batter until finished. Right before serving, stir yogurt into berry mixture and mix well. Drizzle fruity yogurt sauce over pancakes instead of maple syrup and butter.

Per serving (2 pancakes) 240 Cal, 2.5 g Fat, 0 g Trans Fat, 1 g Sat Fat, 5 mg Chol, 530 mg Sod, 47 g Carb, 4 g Fib, 9 g Prot, 20% Calc. **POINTS** value: 4.

express lane Dry pancake mix (flour, baking soda, and cornmeal) can be made in large batches ahead of time, kept in an airtight glass jar or plastic container, and stored for up to 2 months.

BAKED BLUEBERRY-PEACH FRENCH TOAST

> **16 slices Weight Watchers 100% Whole Wheat Bread**
>
> 1 cup fresh blueberries, or 1 cup frozen, thawed blueberries
>
> 1 large peach, chopped, or 1 cup frozen, thawed peach slices
>
> 2½ cups fat-free skim milk
>
> 2 cups fat-free egg substitute
>
> 2 tablespoons sugar, granulated
>
> 1 teaspoon ground cinnamon
>
> 1 teaspoon vanilla extract
>
> 1 tablespoon powdered sugar

Hands-On Prep 12 minutes

Cook 30 minutes

Serves 8

Makes 8 slices

3 POINTS VALUE

1 Preheat oven to 400°F.

2 Arrange 8 slices of bread in the bottom of a 9 × 13-inch baking dish, squishing slices together to make one layer; sprinkle blueberries and peaches over top.

3 In a medium bowl, whisk together milk, egg substitute, granulated sugar, cinnamon, and vanilla extract. Pour half of milk mixture over fruit; top with remaining 8 slices of bread. Pour remaining milk mixture over bread; using a spatula, press top layer of bread slices down to saturate with milk mixture.

4 Cover dish with foil and bake 20 minutes; uncover dish and bake until egg mixture is set and top is golden brown, about 10 minutes more. Cool slightly before sifting powdered sugar over top. Slice into 8 pieces and serve.

Per Serving (1 piece): 200 Cal, 3.5 g Fat, 0 g Sat Fat, 0 g Trans Fat, 0 mg Chol, 320 mg Sod, 30 g Carb, 6 g Fib, 16 g Prot. 25% Calc. **POINTS** value: **3**

good idea You can prepare this recipe in advance, cover it with plastic wrap, and refrigerate it up to 24 hours. When you're ready to cook it, replace the plastic wrap with foil and bake as directed.

V ORANGE-BANANA YOGURT CHILLER

**2 cups Tropicana Light 'n Healthy Orange
Juice Beverage**

2 medium frozen ripe bananas, cut into
pieces

**1 (6-ounce) container Weight Watchers
Nonfat Vanilla Yogurt**

Hands-On Prep **5 minutes**

Cook **about 2 minutes (just
gets blended)**

Serves **4**

1 Place orange juice beverage, bananas, and nonfat vanilla yogurt in
blender. Cover and blend until smooth.

2 Pour into glasses. Serve immediately or refrigerate until ready to use.

Per serving (1 cup): 100 Cal, 0 g Fat, 0 g Sat Fat, 0 g Trans Fat, 0 mg Chol, 30 mg Sod, 24 g Carb, 2 g Fib, 2 g Prot, 10%
Calc. **POINTS** value: **2.**

try it Peel and slice bananas before placing in freezer. Place in tightly
sealed container or bag.

WISE

tastiness

Orange juice Orange juice is good for your body. Everyone knows that. But what you might not know is that you can enjoy the great taste and nutritional punch from Tropicana, without adding up all those **POINTS** values.

Now it's easier than ever to get going in the morning with a glass of Tropicana Light 'n Healthy Orange Juice Beverage—just one glass has half the sugar and calories of regular orange juice! With two delicious and nutritious varieties, Tropicana Light 'n Healthy Orange Juice Beverage gives your body what it needs—extra calcium, extra vitamin C, and a ton of delicious, freshly squeezed flavor.

Need more servings of fruit during the day? Pour a glass of orange juice beverage into a portable bottle, add some ice to keep it cool, and bring it with you on the go. Now that's a smart choice to keep you on track.

Tropicana Light 'n Healthy Calcium, and Tropicana Light 'n Healthy Some Pulp—only 1 **POINTS** value each!

TASTY SUGGESTIONS
Who says orange juice is just for drinking? Throw some Tropicana Light 'n Healthy Orange Juice Beverage in your favorite baked recipes, from crêpes to muffins, for a tasty, tangy flavor twist.

V EGGS FLORENTINE

4 large egg whites

1 teaspoon water

⅛ teaspoon salt

⅛ teaspoon pepper

1 teaspoon red onion, finely minced

1 cup packed baby spinach leaves

2 slices Weight Watchers Cheese Singles

1 Weight Watchers Wheat English Muffin, split and toasted

Hands-On Prep **5 minutes**

Cook **15 minutes**

Serves **2**

Makes **1 English muffin**

2 POINTS VALUE

1 Combine egg whites, water, salt, and pepper in a small bowl and set aside. Do not whisk or beat egg whites.

2 Heat a medium nonstick sauté pan over medium-high heat and lightly coat with nonstick spray. Add red onion and sauté until soft, 1–2 minutes. Stir in spinach and continue cooking until spinach wilts, 1–2 minutes. Add egg-white mixture and cook until egg whites are opaque, about 3 minutes; using a large spatula, flip over and cook until other side is done, 1–2 minutes. Push eggs and vegetables with spatula to middle of pan and turn off heat. Place Weight Watchers Cheese Singles over eggs until melted, 1–2 minutes. Using spatula, divide and scoop equal amounts egg-and-vegetable mixture onto each English muffin half.

Per serving (½ muffin): 140 Cal, 3 g Fat, 1.5 g Sat Fat, 0 g Trans Fat, 10 mg Chol, 670 mg Sod, 15 g Carb, 5 g Fib, 15 g Prot, 30% Calc. **POINTS** value: **2.**

try it Don't limit yourself to just spinach for this easy, healthier take on Eggs Benedict. Try using different vegetables such as broccoli, bell peppers, or mushrooms with your eggs.

V BREAKFAST VEGGIE CASSEROLE

2 slices Weight Watchers 100% Whole Wheat Bread

3 tablespoons red onion, diced

3 tablespoons red bell pepper, diced

3 tablespoons zucchini, diced

2 large eggs

2 large egg whites

⅛ teaspoon salt

⅛ teaspoon pepper

2 tablespoons Weight Watchers Reduced Fat Shredded Cheddar Cheese

Hands-On Prep **10 minutes**

Cook **30 minutes**

Serves **2**

Makes **2 ramekins**

3 POINTS VALUE

1 Preheat oven to 400°F. Lightly coat 2 oven-safe, 8-ounce ramekins (3½ inches in diameter) with nonstick spray. Cut a circle from each slice of bread and firmly press into bottoms of both ramekins. Set aside.

2 Lightly coat a medium sauté pan with nonstick spray and heat over medium-high heat. Add onion, bell pepper, and zucchini, and sauté until vegetables soften and onion is translucent, 3–5 minutes. Remove from heat promptly and set aside.

3 In a medium bowl, whisk together eggs, egg whites, salt, and pepper until well combined. Stir in cooked vegetables and cheese, and pour equal amounts egg-and-vegetable mixture over bread circles into each ramekin. Bake uncovered until a knife inserted into center comes out clean, about 20 minutes. Remove promptly and let sit for 5–10 minutes before serving.

Per serving (1 ramekin): 170 Cal, 7 g Fat, 2.5 g Sat Fat, 0 g Trans Fat, 210 mg Chol, 410 mg Sod, 12 g Carb, 3 g Fib, 15 g Prot, 15% Calc. **POINTS** value: **3.**

express lane Want to avoid too much early-morning prep? Sauté vegetables and whisk eggs the night before. Combine ingredients, cover, and store in refrigerator overnight. Then just preheat oven, cut bread circles, and pour mixture into ramekins when you're ready for breakfast the next morning.

BREAKFAST PIZZA
WITH TURKEY SAUSAGE

¼ pound turkey sausage, sliced

4 large egg whites

½ teaspoon water

⅛ teaspoon salt

⅛ teaspoon pepper

> **1 Weight Watchers Wheat English Muffin, split and lightly toasted**

> **2 tablespoons Weight Watchers Reduced Fat Shredded Cheddar Cheese, divided**

Hands-On Prep 10 minutes

Cook 15 minutes

Serves 2 (1 English muffin half per serving)

Makes 1 English muffin

5 POINTS VALUE

1 Heat a small nonstick sauté pan over medium-high heat and lightly coat with nonstick spray. Add turkey sausage and cook, turning sausage slices for even heating, until sausage is fully cooked, about 7 minutes. Transfer sausage slices to a plate and set aside. Wipe pan clean with a damp cloth and set aside to cool slightly.

2 In a small mixing bowl, whisk together egg whites, water, salt, and pepper. Heat same sauté pan over medium heat and lightly coat with nonstick spray. Add egg-white mixture and gently scramble eggs until done, 1–2 minutes. Remove pan from heat promptly.

3 Place equal amounts cooked sausage slices onto each English muffin half. Place equal amounts scrambled egg whites onto each English muffin half and top each English muffin half with 1 tablespoon cheese. Place mini-pizzas in broiler or toaster oven until cheese melts, about 1 minute. Remove from heat promptly and serve immediately.

Per serving (½ muffin): 240 Cal, 12 g Fat, 6 g Sat Fat, 0 g Trans Fat, 35 mg Chol, 740 mg Sod, 12 g Carb, 3 g Fib, 21 g Prot, 10% Calc. **POINTS** value: **5.**

health smarts Leaner breakfast meats such as turkey sausage, Canadian bacon, or turkey bacon are significantly lower in fat and calories compared to traditional breakfast meats made with pork or beef. When available, choose turkey sausage made with white meat (breast meat) only.

INDIVIDUAL HAM, CHEESE, AND VEGGIE FRITTATAS

1 pound frozen hash brown potatoes, thawed

4 large egg, beaten

1 tablespoon fat-free skim milk

⅛ teaspoon salt, or to taste

⅛ teaspoon pepper, or to taste

2 ounces cooked lean ham, finely chopped

2 tablespoons sweet red pepper, finely chopped

2 tablespoons green pepper, finely chopped

2 tablespoons onion, finely chopped

> ½ cup Weight Watchers Reduced Fat Shredded Cheese

Hands-On Prep 15 minutes

Cook 25 minutes

Serves 8

Makes 8 frittatas

1 Preheat oven to 350°F. Coat 8 muffin tin holes with nonstick spray. Spread potatoes around bottom and press potato up sides of each muffin hole; place in oven and cook for 10 minutes.

2 Meanwhile, beat eggs and milk together in a medium bowl; season with salt and pepper. Add ham, peppers, onion, and cheese to bowl; mix to combine.

3 Remove potatoes from oven (after cooking for 10 minutes) and press potatoes down firmly with a spoon so that they are spread out like mini pie crusts (potatoes should cover bottom and sides of each hole). Pour about ⅛ cup of egg mixture into the center of each muffin hole.

4 Return pan to oven and cook until potatoes are crisp and golden, and the egg mixture is set, about 15 minutes. Remove from oven and let sit about 5 minutes before serving.

Per serving (1 frittata): 110 Cal, 4 g Fat, 1.5 g Sat Fat, 0 g Trans Fat, 110 mg Chol, 115 mg Sod, 10 g Carb, 1 g Fib, 8 g Prot, 4% Calc. **POINTS** value: **2.**

2

Chicken and Chile Wraps,
page 39

TAKE IT *with you*

30 Chilled Fruit Soup To-Go
   with Yogurt

33 Mango Pudding

34 Sliced Apple Napolean

36 Vegetable Kabobs
   with Spinach–Blue Cheese Dip

37 Lentil Salad with Fresh Mint
   and Goat Cheese

38 Curry Chicken Salad

39 Chicken and Chile Wraps

40 Turkey Bagel-Sandwich
   with Avocado and Green Apple

42 Lean Ham Sandwich with
   Edamame Spread

44 Grilled Veggie Pocket with Fresh
   Herb Pesto

46 Eggplant-Mozzarella Panini with
   Sun-Dried Tomato Spread

47 Teriyaki Snack Mix

CHILLED FRUIT SOUP TO-GO WITH YOGURT

½ cup strawberries, hulled and sliced

½ cup blueberries

½ cup raspberries

½ cup blackberries

1 cup Tropicana Light 'n Healthy Orange Juice Beverage

½ unpeeled apple, diced

1 (6-ounce) container Weight Watchers Nonfat Vanilla Yogurt

Hands-On Prep 10 minutes

Serves 2 (1⅓ cups per serving)

Makes 2⅔ cups

Combine all berries and orange juice beverage in food processor. Purée on medium-high power until semi-smooth and liquified. Stir in diced apple and yogurt until fully incorporated. Transfer to Thermos or plastic container with secure lid. Keep fruit soup chilled until ready to eat.

Per serving (1⅓ cups): 150 Cal, 1 g Fat, 0 g Sat Fat, 1 g Trans Fat, 5 mg Chol, 55 mg Sod, 35 g Carb, 6 g Fib, 4 g Prot, 10% Calc. **POINTS** value: **2.**

good idea Keep your fruit soup chilled all day in a Thermos until you're ready for a refreshing midday pick-me-up packed with antioxidants.

CLEVER *creaminess*

Yogurt Research shows that eating yogurt is a great way to add protein and calcium to your diet. All Weight Watchers Yogurts also have prebiotics and probiotics. Prebiotics are food components that stimulate the growth of "good bacteria" called probiotics. Consuming probiotics is thought to increase the number of good bacteria in the digestive system, while at the same time reducing harmful bacteria. But these yogurts aren't just good for you—they taste great, too!

Weight Watchers Yogurts are a smart and delicious choice any time of day, whether it be part of breakfast, lunch, or a midday snack, or added to your favorite recipe.

TASTY SUGGESTIONS
Make dips with yogurt instead of sour cream. Pour your favorite yogurt flavor into a plastic storage container, cut up some fresh fruit and vegetables and store them separately. Take this tasty snack on the go to keep those midday munchies at bay.

V MANGO PUDDING

1¼ cups mango nectar

¾ cup 2% reduced-fat milk

4 tablespoons cornstarch

1 large mango, diced, divided

1 tablespoon fresh mint leaves, slivered

Hands-On Prep **7 minutes**

Cook **6 minutes**

Serves **4** (½ cup pudding and 1 tablespoon fresh mango per serving)

Makes **6 cups pudding and 4 tablespoons fresh mango**

1 Pour nectar into a medium saucepan; place over medium heat.

2 Place milk and cornstarch in a medium mixing bowl; stir to combine and slowly pour into mango nectar, stirring continuously. Increase heat to medium-high and continue stirring until thick, 4–5 minutes. Remove from heat and stir ½ of mango into mixture; pour pudding into four ½-cup custard cups. Refrigerate pudding for at least 2 hours or up to overnight.

3 Combine remaining mango with mint and spoon over chilled pudding.

Per serving (½ cup & 1 tablespoon mango): 130 Cal, 1 g Fat, 0.5 g Sat Fat, 0 g Trans Fat, 5 mg Chol, 25 mg Sod, 29 g Carb, 1 g Fib, 2 g Prot, 8% Calc. **POINTS** value: **2.**

SLICED APPLE NAPOLEAN

2 slices turkey bacon

½ teaspoon light maple syrup

3 thin slices unpeeled Granny Smith apple

2 pieces Weight Watchers Reduced Fat Cheddar Cheese Snacks

Hands-On Prep **5 minutes**

Cook **2 minutes**

Serves **1**

Makes **1 Napolean**

4 POINTS VALUE

1 Line a microwavable plate with a paper towel. Place bacon on paper towel and lightly brush with maple syrup. Heat in microwave on high power until bacon is thoroughly cooked, 1–2 minutes.

2 On a separate plate, layer a slice of apple, a piece of cheese, and a slice of turkey bacon that has been cut in half. Repeat with another slice of apple, remaining piece of cheese, and remaining slice of turkey bacon cut in half. Top with remaining apple slice. Wrap securely in plastic wrap and take it with you.

Per serving (1 Napolean): 200 Cal, 9 g Fat, 4 g Sat Fat, 0 g Trans Fat, 65 mg Chol, 610 mg Sod, 12 g Carb, 2 g Fib, 19 g Prot, 20% Calc. **POINTS** value: **4.**

good idea For a satisfying afternoon snack, enjoy this sweet 'n' savory bite with a glass of refreshing iced apple-cinnamon tea.

V VEGETABLE KABOBS WITH SPINACH–BLUE CHEESE DIP

2 cups fresh spinach, chopped (about 1 ounce)

1 cup water

½ cup fat-free sour cream

⅛ cup blue cheese, crumbled

⅛ teaspoon pepper

2 large zucchini, trimmed

2 large yellow summer squash, trimmed

16 small cremini mushrooms, cleaned and trimmed

¼ teaspoon salt

¼ teaspoon pepper

Hands-On Prep **15** minutes

Cook **7** minutes

Serves **8** (1 large skewer or 2 small skewers and about 2 tablespoons of dip per serving)

Makes **8** large kabobs or **16** small kabobs

1 POINTS VALUE

1 To prepare dip, place spinach in a small saucepan with water. Cook over high heat for 1 minute; drain well. Place spinach in a small serving bowl; stir in sour cream, blue cheese, and ⅛ teaspoon pepper. Set dip aside.

2 Preheat grill to high. To prepare kabobs, cut each zucchini and squash in half lengthwise and then cut each half into eight ½-inch-thick slices. Arrange zucchini, yellow squash, and mushrooms on eight 12-inch or sixteen 6-inch metal skewers using 2 pieces of each vegetable per 12-inch skewer or 1 piece of each vegetable per 6-inch skewer. Lightly coat skewers with olive oil nonstick spray; season with salt and pepper. (If using wooden skewers, make sure to soak them in water for 30 minutes to prevent charring.)

3 Grill kabobs until squash is tender and lightly browned, 2–3 minutes per side. Serve kabobs with dip.

Per serving (1 large kabob or 2 small kabobs and 2 tablespoons dip): 70 Cal, 2 g Fat, 1 g Sat Fat, 0 g Trans Fat, 5 mg Chol, 180 mg Sod, 10 g Carb, 2 g Fib, 5 g Prot, 8% Calc. **POINTS** value: **1**.

try it Long, thin Japanese eggplant is also excellent when matched with blue cheese dip. Use the eggplant instead of the yellow squash following the same directions as above.

V LENTIL SALAD WITH FRESH MINT AND GOAT CHEESE

1 cup dry lentils, French green variety, washed and picked over to remove debris

1 tablespoon bay leaf

¼ cup red onion, coarsely chopped

3 tablespoons fresh mint leaves, coarsely chopped

¼ teaspoon salt, or to taste

¼ teaspoon pepper, freshly ground, or to taste

¼ cup semisoft goat cheese, crumbled

Hands-On Prep **10 minutes**

Cook **20 minutes**

Serves **4** (about ½ cup per serving)

Makes **2 cups**

3 POINTS VALUE

1. Place lentils in a medium saucepan and pour over enough water to cover lentils by 2 to 3 inches. Add bay leaf and set pan over high heat; bring to a boil. Reduce heat to medium and partially cover pan; simmer until lentils are tender, 15–20 minutes. Drain lentils; discard bay leaf and transfer lentils to a large bowl.

2. While lentils are still warm, stir in red onion and mint; season to taste with salt and pepper. Sprinkle cheese over salad just before serving; serve warm or chilled.

Per serving (about ½ cup): 180 Cal, 3 g Fat, 1.5 g Sat Fat, 0 g Trans Fat, 5 mg Chol, 190 mg Sod, 29 g Carb, 7 g Fib, 12 g Prot, 4% Calc. **POINTS** value: **3.**

good idea If you add the cheese while the lentils are still hot, it will melt and be tasted but not be visible.

Turn this side dish into a complete meal by adding ½ pound of cooked medium shrimp or 2 cups of diced cooked chicken.

Try swapping fresh parsley for the mint leaves for a nice flavor change.

CURRY CHICKEN SALAD

2 teaspoons salt

½ pound skinless boneless chicken breast

> **3 tablespoons Weight Watchers Reduced Fat Whipped Cream Cheese Spread**

¼ teaspoon curry powder

1 teaspoon shallot or red onion, minced

2 tablespoons carrot, finely diced

2 tablespoons green apple, finely diced

Hands-On Prep 10 minutes

Cook 30 minutes

Serves 2 (½ cup per serving)

Makes 1 cup salad

4 POINTS VALUE

1 Fill a medium pot about ¾ full with water and add salt. Bring to a rapid boil and submerge chicken breast in boiling water. Cook uncovered on medium-high heat until chicken is cooked all the way through, about 25 minutes. Transfer chicken to plate and cool uncovered in refrigerator.

2 Meanwhile, in a medium bowl, combine cream cheese, curry powder, shallot, carrot, and apple. Mix well until all ingredients are fully incorporated; set aside.

3 Dice cooled chicken into small cubes and add to salad. Mix until chicken is well coated, transfer to plastic container with secure lid, and take it with you. Can be served alone or with bread.

Per serving (½ cup): 180 Cal, 5 g Fat, 3 g Sat Fat, 0 g Trans Fat, 75 mg Chol, 420 mg Sod, 5 g Carb, 1 g Fib, 27 g Prot, 2% Calc. **POINTS** value (salad only): 4.

good idea For a portable version of this delicious, satisfying lunch, scoop ½ cup of chicken salad into a Weight Watchers 100% Whole Wheat Pita Pocket. Top with shredded lettuce and diced tomato. **POINTS** value will increase to a **POINTS** value of 5 per serving.

CHICKEN AND CHILE WRAPS

1 small poblano chile

¼ cup reduced-calorie mayonnaise

4 medium whole-wheat tortillas

1 cup romaine lettuce, chopped

12 ounces cooked skinless boneless chicken breast, cut into strips

2 tablespoon fresh chives, minced

½ medium avocado, sliced

Hands-On Prep **20 minutes**

Cook 5 minutes

Serves 4 (1 wrap per serving)

Makes 4 wraps

8 POINTS VALUE

1 Place chile over stovetop flame; char on all sides, about 5 minutes (be careful not to burn your hands). Remove chile from flame and place in a paper bag; close bag and set aside to steam for 15 minutes. Remove chile from bag and remove blackened skin with your hands, under running water. Core, seed, and chop chile; set aside.

2 Spread 1 tablespoon of mayonnaise over each tortilla and top each with ¼ cup of lettuce. Arrange ¼ of cooked chicken in a strip down the center of each tortilla; top each with ¼ of chile, chives, and avocado.

3 To serve, fold the bottom third of each tortilla toward the middle. Then fold the left side to the center and the right side to the center; serve.

Per serving (1 wrap): 380 Cal, 15 g Fat, 2 g Sat Fat, 0 g Trans Fat, 70 mg Chol, 350 mg Sod, 27 g Carb, 5 g Fib, 32 g Prot, 2% Calc. **POINTS** value: **8.**

express lane To make this zesty wrap in minutes, substitute a small can of roasted mild chiles for the poblano chile, a cup of baby salad greens for the romaine, and refrigerated, cooked chicken strips for the roasted chicken.

TURKEY BAGEL-SANDWICH WITH AVOCADO AND GREEN APPLE

> 2 tablespoons Weight Watchers Reduced Fat Whipped Cream Cheese Spread

> 1 Weight Watchers Bagel, lightly toasted and halved

2 ounces reduced-sodium roast turkey breast, thinly sliced (deli-style)

2 thin slices unpeeled Granny Smith apple

3 thin slices ripe avocado

Hands-On Prep 10 minutes

Serves 1

7 POINTS VALUE

Spread cream cheese evenly over both sides of toasted bagel. Layer turkey, apple, and avocado onto bottom half of bagel. Top with remaining bagel half, wrap securely with plastic wrap, and take it with you.

Per serving (1 sandwich): 340 Cal, 13 g Fat, 5 g Sat Fat, 0 g Trans Fat, 35 mg Chol, 880 mg Sod, 43 g Carb, 13 g Fib, 21 g Prot, 10% Calc. *POINTS* value: 7.

health smarts Avocados contribute almost 20 vitamins, minerals, and beneficial plant compounds, as well as heart-healthy polyunsaturated and monounsaturated fats. Enjoy the avocado's health benefits and delicate, nutty flavor by spreading a thin slice on toast instead of butter, or use a few thin slices in sandwiches in place of mayonnaise.

LEAN HAM SANDWICH WITH EDAMAME SPREAD

6 cups water

1 (16-ounce) bag frozen shelled edamame (soybeans)

½ teaspoon salt

½ teaspoon pepper

2 tablespoons lemon juice

> **2 tablespoons Weight Watchers Reduced Fat Whipped Cream Cheese Spread**

> **2 slices Weight Watchers Multi-Grain Bread**

2 ounces lean ham, thinly sliced

Hands-On Prep 10 minutes

Cook 10 minutes

Makes 1 sandwich and 15 servings Edamame Spread (each serving of spread is 2 tablespoons)

Makes 2 cups spread

4 POINTS VALUE

1 Bring water to a rapid boil in a medium pot. Cook edamame according to package instructions. When soybeans are done, set aside about 1 cup hot water from pot. Drain edamame thoroughly. In a food processor, combine edamame, salt, pepper, lemon juice, and cream cheese. Pulse on medium-high speed until smooth, pausing occasionally to add 3–4 tablespoons saved hot water to edamame mixture.

2 Transfer edamame spread from food processor to covered container and cool in refrigerator. When spread is cooled, spread 1 tablespoon edamame spread on each slice of bread. Assemble sandwich with ham slices. Wrap sandwich securely with plastic wrap, and take it with you.

Per serving (2 tablespoons spread, 2 ounces lean ham, 2 slices bread): 200 Cal, 4 g Fat, 0.5 g Sat Fat, 0 g Trans Fat, 30 mg Chol, 720 mg Sod, 22 g Carb, 6 g Fib, 19 Prot, 8% Calc. **POINTS** value: **4.**

good idea This recipe doesn't have to be limited to sandwiches. Use remaining edamame spread as a healthy dip for your favorite raw veggies or rice crackers. Keep in mind that 1 teaspoon of the edamame spread has a **POINTS** value of 1 per serving.

V GRILLED VEGGIE POCKET WITH FRESH HERB PESTO

1 cup red onion, thinly sliced

1 small zucchini, cut into thin strips

pinch salt

pinch pepper

¼ cup packed fresh basil leaves

½ garlic clove

1 tablespoon reduced-fat grated Parmesan cheese

2 tablespoons plain low-fat yogurt

¼ teaspoon lemon juice

2 teaspoons pignoli nuts

1 Weight Watchers 100% Whole Wheat Pita Pocket, toasted

Hands-On Prep **15 minutes**

Cook **30 minutes**

Serves **1**

Makes **1 sandwich, 1 tablespoon pesto**

5 POINTS VALUE

1 Preheat oven to 350°F. Lightly coat a baking sheet with nonstick spray. Arrange red onion and zucchini in a single layer across baking sheet; season with salt and pepper. Roast until vegetables soften, about 25 minutes. Remove from heat promptly and set aside to cool slightly.

2 Meanwhile, to make the pesto, combine basil leaves, garlic, cheese, and yogurt in a food processor and pulse on medium-high speed until smooth and well blended. Transfer mixture to medium bowl and stir in lemon juice and pignoli nuts. Add vegetables and toss to coat. Spoon vegetable-pesto mixture into pita pocket, wrap securely in foil, and take it with you.

Per serving (1 sandwich): 260 Cal, 7 g Fat, 0.5 g Sat Fat, 0 g Trans Fat, 10 mg Chol, 550 mg Sod, 46 g Carb, 13 g Fib, 13 g Prot, 20% Calc. **POINTS** value: **5.**

food note Pesto is traditionally made with more pignoli nuts, Parmesan cheese, and of course, plenty of olive oil. Ours is a slimmed-down version of the classic Italian favorite, with minimum calories and maximum flavor. Make a larger batch of this aromatic pesto and toss with whole wheat pasta.

INTELLIGENT

heartiness

Bread Enjoying the taste of fresh bread is easier than ever! Weight Watchers Breads, Bagels, Rolls, Pitas, and English Muffins are low in *POINTS* values, and full of delicious flavor. Each is a good source of fiber—between 4 and 9 grams per serving—more than traditional bread offerings in your supermarket aisle.

Weight Watchers Bread products are a smart choice for your morning toast, midday sandwich, or entertaining snacks.

English Muffins, 100% Whole Wheat Bread, Multi-Grain Bread, Rye Bread, and Whole Wheat Pita Pockets—only 1 *POINTS* value each! Bagels and Wheat Sandwich Rolls —only 2 *POINTS* value each!

TASTY SUGGESTIONS
Toast a slice of Multi-Grain Bread and top it with your favorite fruit spread in the morning, or pop open a Whole Wheat Pita Pocket and stuff it with hummus and raw vegetables for a delicious after-school snack!

V EGGPLANT-MOZZARELLA PANINI WITH SUN-DRIED TOMATO SPREAD

2 thick slices eggplant, about 3½ inches in diameter

2 thick slices red bell pepper

pinch salt

pinch pepper

1½ teaspoons olive oil, divided

1 cup water

4 pieces sun-dried tomatoes, dried (avoid sun-dried tomatoes in oil)

½ teaspoon red wine vinegar

½ teaspoon Dijon mustard

2 slices Weight Watchers 100% Whole Wheat Bread, toasted

3 tablespoons Weight Watchers Reduced Fat Shredded Mozzarella Cheese

Hands-On Prep 15 minutes

Cook 30 minutes

Serves 1

Makes 1 sandwich, about 2 tablespoons spread

5 POINTS VALUE

1 Preheat oven to 350°F. Lightly coat a baking sheet with nonstick spray. Arrange eggplant and red pepper slices in a single layer across baking sheet. Season with salt and pepper, and drizzle ½ teaspoon olive oil evenly over vegetables. Roast until vegetables are soft, about 25 minutes. Remove from heat promptly and set aside to cool slightly.

2 Meanwhile, to make the spread, bring water to a boil in a small pan. Place sun-dried tomatoes in a small bowl. Pour in boiling water and let sit until tomatoes soften and rehydrate, about 5 minutes. Do not discard hot water. Combine remaining 1 teaspoon olive oil, red wine vinegar, Dijon mustard, softened tomatoes, and 1 teaspoon saved hot water in a food processor and pulse on medium-high speed until ingredients are thoroughly mixed.

3 To assemble sandwich, spread sun-dried tomato mixture on 1 slice of toast. Sprinkle cheese evenly across tomato spread, then place vegetables on top of cheese. Top with remaining slice of toast and press down gently. Wrap securely with foil and take it with you.

Per serving (1 sandwich): 240 Cal, 11 g Fat, 2.5 g Sat Fat, 0 g Trans Fat, 10 mg Chol, 620 mg Sod, 29 g Carb, 9 g Fib, 12 g Prot, 25% Calc. **POINTS value: 5**.

good idea A larger batch of sun-dried tomato spread can also be made ahead of time and stored in an airtight plastic container in the refrigerator for up to 3 days.

TERIYAKI SNACK MIX

2 cups General Mills® Multi-Bran Chex, or similar product

1 cup soybean nuts

1 cup ready-to-eat puffed rice cereal

½ cup slivered almonds

2½ tablespoons teriyaki sauce

2½ teaspoons vegetable oil

1½ teaspoons sesame oil

2 teaspoons ground ginger

1 teaspoon wasabi powder

Hands-On Prep 5 minutes

Cook 8 minutes

Serves 8 (½ cup per serving)

Makes 4 cups

1 Preheat oven to 375°F.

2 In a large bowl, combine Chex, soybean nuts, puffed rice cereal, and almonds. Combine remaining ingredients in a small bowl. Pour wet ingredients over dry ingredients and toss to coat; spread on a large baking sheet.

3 Bake, stirring after 5 minutes, until lightly brown and crispy, 2–3 minutes more. Remove from oven and let cool.

Per serving (about ½ cup): 210 Cal, 11 g Fat, 1.5 g Sat Fat, 0 g Trans Fat, 0 mg Chol, 270 mg Sod, 21 g Carb, 6 g Fib, 10 g Prot, 6% Calc. **POINTS** value: **4.**

3

Chicken Fingers with Ranch Dip
and Seasoned Fries, page 64

DINNER
for one

50 Summertime Panzanella Salad

52 Hot Tuna Melt on English Muffin

54 Reuben Sandwich

56 Lamb Gyro with Cucumber Dill Sauce

58 Veggie Burrito with Black Beans and Avocado Salsa

59 Grilled Pizza with Chicken Sausage, Onions, and Sweet Peppers

60 Beef and Vegetable Stroganoff–Topped Potato

62 Spiced Carrot Soup

63 Mac 'n Cheese

64 Chicken Fingers with Ranch Dip and Seasoned Fries

65 Stir-Fried Chicken with Broccoli, Red Peppers, and Cashews

66 Home-Style Turkey Meatloaf

67 Pan-Roasted Cod with Orange "Beurre Blanc"

68 Pan-Seared Salmon with Basil-Dijon Cream Sauce

V SUMMERTIME PANZANELLA SALAD

1 medium tomato, coarsely diced

> **2 slices Weight Watchers Multi-Grain Bread, toasted and cut into small squares (include crusts)**

1 cup packed baby spinach leaves

¼ cup frozen corn, thawed and drained

1 stalk green onion, finely chopped

1 tablespoon fresh basil, coarsely chopped

⅛ teaspoon salt

pinch pepper

1½ teaspoons extra virgin olive oil

1 teaspoon vinegar of choice

Hands-On Prep 15 minutes

Serves 1

Makes 3 cups

4 POINTS VALUE

1 Combine tomato, bread, spinach, corn, green onion, and basil. Mix well. Season with salt and pepper.

2 In a small bowl, whisk together oil and vinegar. Add dressing to salad and toss to coat. (Avoid soggy bread by dressing salad immediately before eating.)

Per serving (3 cups): 230 Cal, 6 g Fat, 0.5 g Sat Fat, 0 g Trans Fat, 0 mg Chol, 260 mg Sod, 37 g Carb, 8 g Fib, 9 g Prot, 10% Calc. **POINTS** value: 4.

food note The basic components of this rustic Italian salad traditionally include day-old crusty bread, lots of ripe tomatoes, and assorted garden vegetables.

Cut back on calories (and add fiber!) without sacrificing flavor by using Weight Watchers Multi-Grain or 100% Whole Wheat Bread in your panzanella salad.

Serve this salad with grilled shrimp kebabs to make it a satisfying meal.

HOT TUNA MELT ON ENGLISH MUFFIN

½ (5-ounce) can water-packed tuna, drained well (2½ ounces tuna)

¼ cup celery, finely diced

> 1½ tablespoons Weight Watchers Reduced Fat Whipped Cream Cheese Spread

⅛ teaspoon salt

¼ teaspoon pepper

1½ teaspoons lemon juice

> 1 Weight Watchers Wheat English Muffin, halved and lightly toasted

> 1 tablespoon Weight Watchers Reduced Fat Shredded Cheddar Cheese

Hands-On Prep 10 minutes

Cook 1–2 minutes

Serves 1

Makes ½ cup tuna salad, 1 sandwich

5 POINTS VALUE

1 Preheat broiler or toaster oven to high.

2 Combine tuna, celery, cream cheese, salt, pepper, and lemon juice in a small bowl. Mix well until thoroughly combined.

3 Scoop equal parts tuna mixture onto each muffin half. Sprinkle equal amounts cheese over each tuna-topped muffin. Place both halves in broiler or toaster oven and heat until cheese is melted, 1–2 minutes, watching carefully so they do not burn. Remove promptly from heat.

Per serving (1 sandwich): 260 Cal, 6 g Fat, 4 g Sat Fat, 0 g Trans Fat, 35 mg Chol, 870 mg Sod, 26 g Carb, 7 g Fib, 27 g Prot, 15% Calc. **POINTS** value: **5.**

good idea Jazz up plain lettuce or mixed greens with a scoop of this tasty, low-cal tuna salad. Top with Weight Watchers "croutons"—a toasted, cut-up Weight Watchers Wheat English Muffin.

BRILLIANT

tastiness

Cheese Cheesy baked potatoes. Cheesy quesadillas. Bagels with cream cheese. Weight Watchers delicious reduced-fat cheese products are available in eight varieties, five of which come in portion-controlled packages to help you make those smart meal choices and serve the right amount each time.

Can't start your day without that bagel and cream cheese? Do it the smart way—with a toasted Weight Watchers Bagel and the Whipped Cream Cheese Spread. Pack a bowl of your favorite salad to bring to work, and include a serving of the Reduced Fat Shredded Cheddar Cheese—it comes in a handy individual packet filled with rich, delicious cheddar cheese. Or throw a Light String Cheese packet into your gym bag for a post-workout snack to satisfy your hunger.

TASTY SUGGESTIONS
Craving a cheesy pizza? Make it yourself! Toast Weight Watchers English Muffins or Whole Wheat Pita Bread, top them with fresh tomato sauce and some Weight Watchers Reduced Fat Shredded Mozzarella Cheese, then pop 'em in the oven for a warm, gooey, cheesy treat the whole family can enjoy.

REUBEN SANDWICH

> **2 slices Weight Watchers Rye or 100% Whole Wheat Bread**

2 teaspoons grainy deli mustard

3 ounces turkey pastrami, sliced

¼ cup sauerkraut

> **2 tablespoons Weight Watchers Reduced Fat Shredded Mozzarella Cheese**

Hands-On Prep 5 minutes

Cook 8 minutes

Serves 1

Makes 1 sandwich

5 POINTS VALUE

1 Spread mustard on both slices of bread and set aside.

2 Heat a large nonstick pan over medium-high heat. Lightly coat pan with nonstick spray. Add turkey to pan and heat through, about 1½ minutes. Using a spatula, push turkey to one side of pan. Add sauerkraut to pan and stir until heated through, about 2 minutes. Remove from heat, transfer hot turkey and sauerkraut to a plate, set aside, and return pan to heat.

3 Lightly coat pan with nonstick spray. Reduce heat to medium and place 1 slice of bread, mustard side up, into pan. Place turkey onto bread, stack sauerkraut atop turkey, and top with cheese. Carefully place remaining slice of bread, mustard side down, onto cheese and gently press down with spatula for about 2 minutes. Flip sandwich and heat for another 2 minutes. Remove from heat promptly. (To avoid burning bread, do not heat sandwich for more than 2 minutes on either side.)

Per serving (1 sandwich): 240 Cal, 6 g Fat, 2 g Sat Fat, 0 g Trans Fat, 65 mg Chol, 1440 mg Sod, 22 g Carb, 6 g Fib, 23 g Prot, 20% Calc. *POINTS* value: *5.*

good idea For a true delicatessen experience, enjoy this classic sandwich with a kosher pickle and a light coleslaw dressed with olive oil and vinegar instead of mayonnaise. (Coleslaw can add fiber to your meal too!)

LAMB GYRO WITH CUCUMBER DILL SAUCE

pinch salt

pinch pepper

pinch dried oregano

pinch dried thyme

4 ounces boneless leg of lamb, trimmed

2 tablespoons fat-free sour cream

2 tablespoons unpeeled cucumber, finely diced

2 teaspoons fresh dill, chopped

1 teaspoon lemon juice, or to taste

> **1 piece Weight Watchers 100% Whole Wheat Pita Bread, cut in half to form 2 pita pockets**

½ cup romaine or green leaf lettuce, finely chopped

1 roma or plum tomato, chopped

Hands-On Prep 15 minutes

Cook 15 minutes

Serves 1

Makes ⅓ cup sauce

6 POINTS VALUE

1 Rub salt, pepper, oregano, and thyme all over lamb and set aside. Heat medium nonstick skillet or sauté pan over medium-high heat. Lightly coat pan with nonstick spray and place lamb onto center of pan. For medium-rare lamb, cook for 3 minutes on each side. (Cook for a few minutes longer on each side if you prefer more well-done lamb.) Remove from heat promptly and set aside.

2 Meanwhile, combine sour cream, cucumber, dill, and lemon juice. Mix well, season with salt and pepper to taste, and set aside.

3 Slice lamb against the grain into long, thin strips. Open both pita pockets and fill with equal amounts lettuce, tomato, and sliced lamb. Drizzle with sauce.

Per serving (1 pita pocket): 300 Cal, 7 g Fat, 2.5 g Sat Fat, 0 g Trans Fat, 75 mg Chol, 520 mg Sod, 33 g Carb, 11 g Fib, 32 g Prot, 10% Calc. **POINTS** value: **6**.

food note Better known in the United States than in Greece, this popular Greek-American sandwich has its roots in Greek diners and New York City street vendors, and is traditionally made with rotisserie-roasted lamb. The word *gyros* (pronounced jahy-rohs) means "a turn" in Greek, which might refer to the slow spin and rotation of the meat as it is cooking.

VEGGIE BURRITO WITH BLACK BEANS AND AVOCADO SALSA

SALSA

2 tablespoons ripe avocado, diced

1 teaspoon lemon juice

1 roma or plum tomato, diced

1 teaspoon seeded and deveined jalapeño pepper, finely diced (use less jalapeño if you prefer mild salsa), optional

2 teaspoons green onion, chopped

2 teaspoons cilantro, chopped

BURRITO

1 teaspoon olive oil

¼ cup onion, diced

½ teaspoon garlic, minced

½ cup yellow squash, diced

½ cup zucchini, diced

Hands-On Prep 15 minutes

Cook 12 minutes

Serves 1

Makes 1 burrito, about ⅓ cup avocado salsa

10 POINTS VALUE

½ cup canned black beans (do not drain and rinse)

1 small (6- to 8-inch) whole-wheat flour tortilla

> **2 tablespoons Weight Watchers Reduced Fat Shredded Mexican Style Blend**

1 To make the salsa, combine avocado and lemon juice in a small mixing bowl and mix thoroughly. Stir in tomato, jalapeño (if using), green onion, and cilantro until well combined. Cover and chill until ready to serve.

2 To make the burrito filling, heat oil in a large nonstick skillet over medium-high heat. Add onion and garlic and sauté for 2 minutes until onion and garlic are softened. Add squash and zucchini and sauté, stirring regularly to prevent garlic from burning, until vegetables soften, about 3 minutes. Stir in black beans and continue cooking, stirring occasionally, until beans are heated through and ingredients are well combined, about 3 minutes. Remove skillet from heat and set aside. Heat tortilla in microwave on medium power for 10–15 seconds (flour tortillas are easier to work with if warmed).

3 To assemble the burrito, spoon bean mixture onto center of tortilla and sprinkle cheese over bean mixture. Fold bottom of tortilla up to form a base, then fold top of tortilla down towards base. Holding both ends firmly in place, fold in both sides tightly to form burrito shape. (To avoid leaks and maintain shape, wrap bottom half of burrito in foil.) Serve with salsa on the side.

Per serving (1 burrito): 490 Cal, 17 g Fat, 4 g Sat Fat, 0 g Trans Fat, 10 mg Chol, 930 mg Sod, 67 g Carb, 13 g Fib, 19 g Prot, 25% Calc. **POINTS** value: **10**.

GRILLED PIZZA WITH CHICKEN SAUSAGE, ONIONS, AND SWEET PEPPERS

2 links Casual Gourmet® Chicken Sausage—
Pesto, or other brand, halved lengthwise
and thinly sliced

1 small red onion, cut into thin slivers

1 small yellow pepper, cut into ¼-inch-thick
slices

½ cup pizza sauce or tomato sauce

4 medium whole-wheat tortillas

1 teaspoon dried oregano

> **¾ cup Weight Watchers Reduced Fat
> Shredded Mozzarella Cheese**

Hands-On Prep 10 minutes

Cook 15 minutes

Serves 4

Makes 1 pizza
per serving

6 POINTS VALUE

1 Preheat an outdoor grill to medium (or a grill pan over medium-high heat). Place sausage, red onion, and pepper on grill in a grill basket; cook, flipping once, until sausage is golden and vegetables start to brown, 4–6 minutes. Remove from grill and set aside until ready to use.

2 To prepare pizzas, spread 2 tablespoons sauce on each tortilla. Sprinkle each with ¼ teaspoon dried oregano and then top each with ¼ of sausage-vegetable mixture; top each with 3 tablespoons cheese.

3 Place pizzas on grill (or as many as will fit on grill pan at one time) and cook until edges begin to brown, 3–5 minutes; rotate pizzas. Continue cooking until cheese is bubbly, 2–4 minutes more. (If all four pizzas do not fit on grill pan at once, repeat with remaining ingredients.)

Per serving (1 pizza): 300 Cal, 12 g Fat, 3.5 g Sat Fat, 0 g Trans Fat, 45 mg Chol, 760 mg Sod, 27 g Carb, 3 g Fib, 17 g Prot, 15% Calc. **POINTS** value: **6.**

BEEF AND VEGETABLE STROGANOFF–TOPPED POTATO

1 medium baking potato

1 teaspoon olive or vegetable oil

4 ounces beef flank steak, cut across grain
  into thin bite-size strips

1 cup sliced fresh mushrooms

1 small onion, cut into thin wedges

½ teaspoon garlic powder

⅛ teaspoon pepper

> **1 can (18.5-ounce) Progresso® Light Savory
> Vegetable Barley Soup**

¼ cup fat-free sour cream

2 tablespoons fresh parsley, chopped

Hands-On Prep **25 minutes**

Cook **25 minutes**

Serves **2**

Makes ½ potato
per serving

7 POINTS *VALUE*

1 Generously pierce potato with fork. Place on microwavable paper towel. Microwave on High 4–5 minutes, turning once, until tender. Cover; let stand covered 5 minutes.

2 Meanwhile, in 12-inch nonstick skillet, heat oil over high heat. Add beef, mushrooms, and onion; sprinkle with garlic powder and pepper. Cook 5–7 minutes, stirring frequently, just until beef is browned and vegetables begin to soften.

3 Stir in soup. Heat to boiling. Cook uncovered over high heat 7–10 minutes, stirring frequently, until mixture thickens. Remove from heat; stir in sour cream.

4 To serve, place ½ potato on each serving plate. Top each with 1½ cups beef mixture; sprinkle each with 1 tablespoon parsley.

Per serving (½ potato): 330 Cal, 9 g Fat, 3 g Sat Fat, 0 g Trans Fat, 35 mg Chol, 880 mg Sod, 44 g Carb, 7 g Fib, 17 g Prot, 10% Calc. *POINTS* value: **7**.

SENSIBLE

yumminess

Soup What's more enjoyable on a cold, rainy day than a bowl of hot soup? Progresso® Light Soups—with **ZERO POINTS** value per serving—are perfect as part of a light lunch, an accompaniment for dinner, or that soothing snack at the end of the day. Progresso Light Soups offer five delicious soups, brimming with flavor and packed with vegetables and hearty staples like pasta, rice, and corn.

Warm up a bowl of these ready-to-serve soups, or add your favorite flavor to stir-fries, potatoes, meatloaf, and skillet meals for a variety of hearty meal options. Each serving packs in a full serving of vegetables with only .5 grams of fat or less and 60 calories. Now that's one extraordinary meal.

Italian-Style Vegetable, Vegetable & Noodle, Home-Style Vegetable & Rice, Savory Vegetable Barley, and Southwestern-Style Vegetable—all 0 **POINTS** value per serving!

TASTY SUGGESTIONS
Serve Progresso Light Soups as the first course at your next dinner party—just add fresh basil, sage, or rosemary to your favorite variety and you'll have a tasty (and nutritious!) start to the evening.

V SPICED CARROT SOUP

2 teaspoons canola oil

¼ cup shallot or red onion, chopped

½ teaspoon curry powder

⅛ teaspoon chili powder, chipotle variety

29 ounces canned carrots, sliced (undrained)

1 cup buttermilk

¼ teaspoon salt

¼ teaspoon pepper

2 teaspoons fresh lemon juice, divided

¼ cup fat-free sour cream

Hands-On Prep 15 minutes

Cook 4 minutes

Serves 4 (1 cup soup and
1 tablespoon sour cream
per serving)

Makes 4 cups soup
and 4 tablespoons
sour cream

1 Heat oil in a medium saucepan; add shallot, curry powder, and chili powder. Cook over medium heat until shallot is tender, stirring constantly, about 2 minutes. Add carrots, including can liquid, to saucepan.

2 Pour buttermilk into saucepan; swirl milk in pan to 'pick up' any remaining spices. Add salt, pepper, and 1 teaspoon of lemon juice; purée in saucepan using an immersion blender. (Or purée in batches in a blender— careful not to splatter hot liquid.) Taste soup and add remaining teaspoon of lemon juice, if desired.

3 Divide soup among 4 bowls and garnish with sour cream.

Per serving (1 cup soup & 1 tablespoon sour cream): 130 Cal, 4 g Fat, 1 g Sat Fat, 0 g Trans Fat, 5 mg Chol, 300 mg Sod, 19 g Carb, 3 g Fib, 5 g Prot, 15% Calc *POINTS* value: **2**.

Note: We used canned carrots because they cut cooking time considerably (you may use fresh carrots though, if you prefer). If you like a tangy-tasting soup, swap ½ cup of buttermilk for ½ cup of plain fat-free yogurt.

good idea For a festive look, spoon sour cream in the center of each serving. Using a toothpick, draw out "spokes" of sour cream from the center to create a starburst design.

MAC 'N CHEESE

4 cups water

1 cup whole-wheat penne pasta (or whole-wheat pasta of choice)

1 teaspoon unsalted butter

1 tablespoon all-purpose flour

¾ cup fat-free milk

2 tablespoons Weight Watchers Reduced Fat Cream Cheese Spread

¼ teaspoon salt

⅛ teaspoon pepper

¼ cup Weight Watchers Reduced Fat Shredded Cheddar Cheese

Hands-On Prep 5 minutes

Cook 20 minutes

Serves 2 (1 serving = 1 cup)

Makes 2 cups

6 POINTS VALUE

1 In a medium pot, bring water to a rapid boil. Cook pasta according to package instructions, stirring occasionally to prevent pasta from sticking to bottom. When pasta is done, set aside ¼ cup hot pasta-water. Drain pasta thoroughly, and set aside to cool.

2 Heat hot pasta-water and butter in a small pot over medium heat. As butter melts, stir in flour and whisk until fully incorporated and mixture turns light brown, about 3 minutes. Whisk in milk and cream cheese, then season with salt and pepper. Slowly stir in cheddar cheese, whisking constantly, until melted.

3 Reduce heat to low and add pasta to cheese sauce, stirring constantly. Mix well until pasta is thoroughly coated. Remove from heat and let sit and thicken for about 5 minutes before serving.

Per serving (1 cup): 320 Cal, 8 g Fat, 5 g Sat Fat, 0 g Trans Fat, 15 mg Chol, 480 mg Sod, 50 g Carb, 6 g Fib, 16 g Prot, 30% Calc **POINTS** value: **6.**

good idea Make a complete meal but still keep **POINTS** value low by serving this comfort-food favorite with steamed broccoli or spinach and a side of salad. Take the second serving with you for lunch the next day— heat it up in the microwave for a warm meal on the go or in the office.

CHICKEN FINGERS WITH RANCH DIP AND SEASONED FRIES

CHICKEN FINGERS

1 pound uncooked skinless boneless chicken breast, cut into strips

1 tablespoon Dijon mustard

2½ (1-ounce) packets uncooked instant oatmeal(about 1 cup total)

2 teaspoons garlic-herb seasoning, preferably salt-free

½ teaspoon salt

¼ teaspoon pepper

SEASONED FRIES

2 large russet potatoes, peeled and cut into ½-inch-thick fries

1 tablespoon Creole seasoning

½ cup fat-free ranch salad dressing

Hands-On Prep **15** minutes

Cook **30** minutes

Serves **4** (3 ounces of chicken, ½ a potato, and 2 tablespoons of dressing per serving)

Makes **12** ounces of chicken, 2 potatoes and 8 tablespoons of dressing

7 POINTS VALUE

1 Preheat oven to 400°F. Coat a large baking sheet with nonstick spray.

2 Coat chicken strips with mustard. Combine oatmeal, garlic-herb seasoning, salt, and pepper in a shallow dish. Dip chicken strips in oat mixture and turn to coat; place chicken strips on prepared pan.

3 Arrange potatoes around chicken on pan; lightly coat both with nonstick spray. Sprinkle potatoes with Creole seasoning.

4 Bake, flipping once, until chicken is cooked through and both chicken and potatoes are tender and golden brown, about 30 minutes. Serve chicken and potatoes with dressing on the side.

Per serving (3 ounces chicken, ½ a potato and 2 tablespoons dressing): 380 Cal, 3.5 g Fat, 0.5 g Sat Fat, 0 g Trans Fat, 65 mg Chol, 1210 mg Sod, 53 g Carb, 6 g Fib, 33 g Prot, 6% Calc. **POINTS** value: **7.**

STIR-FRIED CHICKEN WITH BROCCOLI, RED PEPPERS, AND CASHEWS

2 teaspoons vegetable oil, divided

1 teaspoon sesame oil, divided

1½ tablespoon ginger root, finely chopped

3 small garlic cloves, finely chopped

1 pound uncooked skinless boneless chicken breast, cut into ½-inch pieces

1 large sweet red pepper, cut into 1-inch pieces

2 cups broccoli florets

2 tablespoons low-sodium soy sauce

20 cashews, roasted, unsalted, roughly chopped

Hands-On Prep 15 minutes

Cook 9 minutes

Serves 4 (1¾ cups per serving)

Makes 7 cups

5 POINTS VALUE

1 Heat a large nonstick skillet over high heat. Add 1 teaspoon vegetable oil, ½ teaspoon sesame oil, ginger, and garlic; cook 15 seconds. Add chicken and stir-fry until starting to brown, 3–4 minutes; transfer to a plate.

2 Add remaining teaspoon vegetable oil, pepper, and broccoli to same skillet; stir-fry for 3 minutes. Add chicken back to skillet, pour in soy sauce and cook, stirring, until chicken is cooked through, about 2 minutes more; toss with remaining ½ teaspoon sesame oil. Sprinkle on cashews and serve.

Per serving (1¾ cups): 230 Cal, 8 g Fat, 1.5 g Sat Fat, 0 g Trans Fat, 65 mg Chol, 390 mg Sod, 9 g Carb, 2 g Fib, 29 g Prot, 4% Calc. **POINTS** value: **5.**

good idea Chop the cashews instead of leaving them whole, to cut back on the total number of nuts used. This still allows you to sprinkle a lot on the dish and keep those **POINTS** values on target!

HOME-STYLE TURKEY MEATLOAF

1 slice Weight Watchers 100% Whole Wheat Bread, toasted

½ pound ground turkey breast (white meat only)

¼ cup Progresso® Light Italian-Style Vegetable Soup

1 large egg white

¼ teaspoon garlic powder

2 tablespoons ketchup, divided

¼ teaspoon salt

¼ teaspoon pepper

Hands-On Prep 10 minutes

Cook 40 minutes

Serves 1

Makes 2 loaves

Serves 2 (1 serving = 1 loaf) (see good idea for how-to use the 2nd loaf)

3 POINTS VALUE

1 Preheat oven to 350°F. Line a baking sheet with foil, lightly coat foil with nonstick spray, and set aside.

2 Break up toasted bread into several small pieces. Place into food processor or blender and briefly pulse at medium-high speed until bread becomes semi-fine bread crumbs.

3 Combine turkey, bread crumbs, soup, egg white, garlic powder, 1 tablespoon ketchup, salt, and pepper in a medium bowl. Mix well until ingredients are thoroughly incorporated. Using clean hands, form and shape mixture into two small loaves. Place loaves onto baking sheet and spread equal amount remaining 1 tablespoon ketchup evenly across tops of both loaves. Bake until internal temperature of both loaves reaches 165°F, 35–40 minutes. Allow to cool slightly before slicing. Wrap leftover meatloaf in foil and store in refrigerator for up to 2 days.

Per serving (1 loaf): 180 Cal, 2 g Fat, 0 g Sat Fat, 0 g Trans Fat, 45 mg Chol, 700 mg Sod, 10 g Carb, 2 g Fib, 32 g Prot, 4% Calc. **POINTS** value: **3**.

good idea Make a delicious next-day sandwich with cold meatloaf. Just layer lettuce, tomato, and sliced meatloaf between toasted Weight Watchers 100% Whole Wheat or Multi-Grain Bread.

PAN-ROASTED COD WITH ORANGE "BEURRE BLANC"

½ cup reduced-sodium vegetable broth

1 tablespoon Tropicana Light 'n Healthy Orange Juice Beverage

1 tablespoon white wine

1 teaspoon shallot or red onion, finely chopped

1 tablespoon Weight Watchers Reduced Fat Whipped Cream Cheese Spread

4 ounces boneless cod or scrod fillet

pinch salt

pinch pepper

Hands-On Prep 8–10 minutes

Cook 20 minutes

Serves 1

Makes 2 tablespoons sauce

3 POINTS VALUE

1. Heat vegetable broth, orange juice beverage, wine, and shallot in a small sauté pan over high heat. Bring to a boil and continue cooking, stirring occasionally, until liquid is reduced to about ¼ cup, 3–5 minutes. Reduce heat to medium-low and whisk in cream cheese. Mixture will look separated, but continue to whisk constantly over low heat until sauce thickens, about 2 minutes. Remove from heat promptly, cover, and keep warm until ready to serve.

2. Season all sides of cod fillet with salt and pepper. Heat a medium sauté pan over medium-high heat and lightly coat with nonstick spray. Place cod (top side down) onto center of pan and cook until slightly golden brown, about 2 minutes. Using a large spatula, flip cod over, reduce heat to medium-low, cover, and continue cooking until internal temperature reaches 145°F, 3–5 minutes. Drizzle warm sauce over cod right before serving.

Per serving (1 fillet & sauce): 150 Cal, 3.5 g Fat, 2 g Sat Fat, 0 g Trans Fat, 55 mg Chol, 410 mg Sod, 6 g Carb, 1 g Fib, 21 g Prot, 4% Calc. **POINTS value: 3.**

food note Making dinner for a guest? This quick and delicious recipe can easily be doubled. Serve with steamed asparagus and baked sweet potato.

PAN-SEARED SALMON WITH BASIL-DIJON CREAM SAUCE

½ teaspoon olive oil

¼ teaspoon garlic, minced

½ teaspoon shallot or red onion, minced

¼ cup dry white wine

1 teaspoon Dijon mustard

¼ cup fat-free milk

> **1 tablespoon Weight Watchers Reduced Fat Whipped Cream Cheese Spread**

2 tablespoons fresh basil, finely chopped into thin ribbons

4 ounces boneless salmon fillet

pinch salt

pinch pepper

Hands-On Prep **10 minutes**

Cook **20 minutes**

Serves **1**

Makes **2 tablespoons** sauce

7
POINTS
VALUE

1 Heat oil in a small sauté pan over medium heat. Add garlic and shallot, stirring constantly, until shallot starts to soften and edges become slightly brown, 2–3 minutes. Immediately add wine and whisk in mustard until fully incorporated. Whisk in milk until fully incorporated, then whisk in whipped cream cheese until fully incorporated. When cream cheese melts, stir in basil and remove from heat promptly. Using a rubber spatula, transfer sauce to a small bowl and set aside.

2 Season all sides of salmon with salt and pepper. Heat same sauté pan over medium-high heat. Lightly coat with nonstick spray. Place salmon (top side down) onto center of pan and cook until slightly browned, 2–3 minutes. Reduce heat to medium-low. Using a large spatula, flip salmon over, cover pan, and continue cooking until internal temperature reaches 140°F, 4–5 minutes. Uncover and remove from heat. Transfer salmon to plate and drizzle sauce over fish.

Per serving (salmon fillet and sauce): 290 Cal, 12 g Fat, 3 g Sat Fat, 0 g Trans Fat, 70 mg Chol, 380 mg Sod, 8 g Carb, 1 g Fib, 25 g Prot, 15% Calc. **POINTS** value: **7**.

food note Salmon is rich in omega-3 fatty acids, which are beneficial for heart health. For a twist on this recipe, you can substitute salmon for tuna, rainbow trout, or Atlantic mackerel, all of which are rich in omega-3 fatty acids.

Grown-Up Creamsicles with White
Wine and Fresh Mint, page 89

CASUAL
entertaining

72 Lemon-Mint Chickpea Dip
   with Pita Chips

73 Endive Spears with Smoked Trout
   and Chive Cream Cheese

74 Italian-Style Veggie Risotto

75 Pasta Salad with Blue Cheese,
   Walnuts, and Arugula

76 Seared Tuna with Soy-Citrus
   Vinaigrette

78 Asian Pork and Vegetable Stir-Fry

79 Lemon-Raspberry Bread Pudding

80 Dark Chocolate Latté
   Milk Shakes

82 Multigrain Waffle Ice Cream
   Sandwiches

84 Chocolate Amaretto
   Cheesecake Pie

86 Individual "Tiramisu" with Fruit

89 Grown-Up Creamsicles
   with White Wine and Fresh Mint

90 Caramel Fondue with Fresh Fruit

LEMON-MINT CHICKPEA DIP WITH PITA CHIPS

PITA CHIPS

2 Weight Watchers 100% Whole Wheat Pita Pockets, split open

½ teaspoon salt

LEMON-MINT CHICKPEA DIP

2 (15½-ounce) cans chickpeas, drained and rinsed)

½ cup water

¼ cup fresh lemon juice

3 tablespoons extra-virgin olive oil

2 large garlic cloves

½ teaspoon salt

Hands-On Prep **12 minutes**

Cook **7 minutes**

Serves **10 servings** (¼ cup dip and 4 pita chips per serving)

Makes: **2½ cups dip and 40 pita chips**

2
POINTS
VALUE

¼ teaspoon cayenne pepper, or to taste

3 tablespoons fresh mint leaves, finely chopped (plus extra for garnish)

2 tablespoons fresh tomatoes, diced

1 To make pita chips, place oven rack in middle position. Preheat oven to 400°F. Line a large baking sheet with foil.

2 Coat both sides of split pitas with olive oil nonstick spray; sprinkle tops with salt. Using a pizza wheel or knife, cut each pita into 8 wedges; place wedges on prepared baking sheet.

3 Bake on middle oven rack until light golden and crisp, 6–7 minutes. Remove to a wire rack to cool.

4 Meanwhile, to make dip, place chickpeas, water, lemon juice, oil, garlic, salt, and cayenne pepper in the bowl of a food processor and process until smooth. Transfer to a bowl and stir in mint. Cover and refrigerate for at least 15 minutes for flavors to blend.

5 To serve, spoon dip into a serving dish. Mound diced tomatoes in center and sprinkle with remaining mint; serve with pita chips.

Per serving (¼ cup dip & 4 pita chips): 140 Cal, 5 g Fat, 0.5 g Sat Fat, 0 g Trans Fat, 0 mg Chol, 550 mg Sod, 18 g Carb, 5 g Fib, 5 g Prot, 4% Calc. **POINTS** value: **2.**

good idea If you are having trouble blending the whole garlic cloves, squeeze them through a garlic press first.

ENDIVE SPEARS WITH SMOKED TROUT AND CHIVE CREAM CHEESE

2 ounces smoked trout

> **½ cup Weight Watchers Reduced Fat Whipped Cream Cheese Spread**

2 tablespoons chopped chives

¼ teaspoon lemon juice

pinch pepper

2 heads endive, trimmed

Hands-On Prep **15 minutes**

Serves **6**

Makes **about 10 tablespoons trout filling (3 endive spears per serving, 4½ teaspoons filling per serving)**

1 POINTS VALUE

1 Place smoked trout in food processor and pulse on medium speed until trout is flaky and puréed. Do not overprocess; trout should not be too soft and mushy.

2 Combine trout, cream cheese, chives, lemon juice, and pepper in a medium bowl and mix well until ingredients are fully incorporated and folded into cream cheese.

3 Cut off endive bottoms and pull leaves off. Spoon about 1½ teaspoons trout filling onto each endive leaf, leaving endive tip clean for picking up with hands. Arrange and serve on a platter.

Per serving (3 endive spears): 90 Cal, 4.5 g Fat, 2.5 g Sat Fat, 0 g Trans Fat, 25 mg Chol, 85 mg Sod, 8 g Carb, 6 g Fib, 6 g Prot, 10% Calc. **POINTS value: 1.**

good idea Experiment with a different flavor by using smoked or cured salmon instead of trout. This recipe also makes a tasty, low-calorie spread for your Weight Watchers Bagel.

ITALIAN-STYLE VEGGIE RISOTTO

1 can (18.5-ounce) Progresso° Light Italian-Style Vegetable Soup, divided

3 cups reduced-sodium vegetable broth, divided

1 tablespoon olive oil

¼ cup onion, finely chopped

1½ cups Arborio rice

6 tablespoons reduced-fat Parmesan cheese, grated

2 teaspoons lemon juice

⅛ teaspoon pepper

Hands-On Prep **10 minutes**
Cook **50 minutes**
Serves **6**
Makes **4¾ cups**

3 POINTS VALUE

1 In a medium saucepan, combine soup and vegetable broth and bring to a gentle boil. Cover and reduce heat to medium-low to keep warm.

2 Heat olive oil over medium-high heat in a 4-quart pot. Add onion and sauté until soft and translucent, 4–5 minutes. Add Arborio rice and sauté briefly, stirring constantly to prevent rice from sticking, until rice is well coated. Stir in 1 cup warm soup-broth mixture. When liquid is absorbed, stir in 1 cup soup-broth mixture and continue cooking, stirring regularly to prevent rice from sticking. Repeat and continue with 1 cup soup-broth mixture at a time, stirring continuously, until all soup-broth mixture is used.

3 Stir in cheese and lemon juice, and reduce heat to medium. When all liquid has been absorbed, taste rice to make sure it is cooked thoroughly. (If you prefer softer rice, stir in 1–2 more cups of broth and repeat instructions above until rice kernels reach desired tenderness.) Remove from heat and season with pepper.

Per serving (about ¾ cup): 160 Cal, 4 g Fat, 0 g Sat Fat, 0 g Trans Fat, 5 mg Chol, 600 mg Sod, 29 g Carb, 2 g Fib, 4 g Prot, 4% Calc. **POINTS** value: **3.**

try it To add some texture and enhance the nutritional value of this flavorful side dish, throw in some of your favorite steamed or sautéed veggies right before serving.

PASTA SALAD WITH BLUE CHEESE, WALNUTS, AND ARUGULA

2 tablespoons walnuts, coarsely chopped

3 quarts water

½ teaspoon salt

6 ounces uncooked bow ties, also called farfalle

2 cups arugula, baby leaves, stems removed

2 tablespoons fresh chives, minced

1 cup grape tomatoes, halved

1 tablespoon white wine vinegar

1 tablespoon extra-virgin olive oil

¼ teaspoon salt

¼ teaspoon pepper

3 tablespoons blue cheese, crumbled

Hands-On Prep 12 minutes

Cook 15 minutes

Serves 4

Makes about 5 cups

5 POINTS VALUE

1 Place walnuts in a small, heavy-bottomed skillet. Toast nuts over medium-high heat until lightly browned, shaking skillet frequently, 1–2 minutes; remove from skillet and set aside.

2 Bring water and ½ teaspoon of salt to a boil in a large pot. Stir in pasta and cook until tender, 11–13 minutes; remove 1 tablespoon of pasta cooking water and save for dressing below. Drain pasta and place in a large serving bowl; immediately add arugula and toss well. Cover bowl with a lid or tight-fitting plastic wrap; set aside until arugula is limp, about 5 minutes. Stir in chives and tomatoes.

3 Stir together vinegar, oil, reserved tablespoon of pasta cooking water, remaining ¼ teaspoon of salt, and pepper in a cup. Pour dressing over pasta salad and toss well; sprinkle with blue cheese.

Per serving (1¼ cups): 240 Cal, 8 g Fat, 2 g Sat Fat, 0 g Trans Fat, 5 mg Chol, 530 mg Sod, 34 g Carb, 2 g Fib, 8 g Prot, 6% Calc. **POINTS** value: **5.**

good idea If you're using mature arugula leaves, chop and add them to the pasta for 1 to 2 minutes at the end of the cooking time to blanch them. Drain the pasta and arugula, and immediately move to the next step of mixing the salad ingredients together.

SEARED TUNA WITH SOY-CITRUS VINAIGRETTE

> ¼ cup Tropicana Light 'n Healthy Orange Juice Beverage

4 teaspoons lemon juice

4 teaspoons reduced-sodium soy sauce

½ tablespoon fresh ginger, peeled and grated

1 teaspoon garlic, finely minced

2 teaspoons shallot or red onion, finely minced

1 tablespoon green onion, finely minced (green part only)

1 teaspoon Dijon mustard

1 pound sashimi-grade yellowfin tuna steak

pinch salt

pinch pepper

1 tablespoon canola or olive oil

Hands-On Prep **30 minutes**

Cook **5 minutes**

Serves **4** (4 ounces tuna per serving and ⅛ cup vinaigrette)

Makes ½ cup vinaigrette

4 POINTS VALUE

1 Whisk together orange juice beverage, lemon juice, soy sauce, ginger, garlic, shallot, green onion, and mustard in a small bowl until mustard is fully incorporated. Continue whisking and slowly add oil in a thin, steady stream until emulsified. Cover and chill until ready to use.

2 Season both sides of tuna steak with salt and pepper to taste.

3 Heat medium nonstick skillet or sauté pan over medium-high heat. Lightly coat with oil and allow pan to get very hot (a drop of water on pan's surface should sizzle and evaporate quickly). Place tuna onto center of pan. For rare tuna, sear for 1–2 minutes on each side. (For medium-rare to medium tuna, sear for 2–5 minutes on each side, depending on thickness of tuna steak.) Remove from heat promptly and set aside to rest and cool for 2 minutes before slicing. Slice tuna against the grain into 4 equal portions (4 ounces per person). Drizzle vinaigrette over tuna right before serving.

Per serving (4 ounces tuna and ⅛ cup vinaigrette): 170 Cal, 4.5 g Fat, 0.5 g Sat Fat, 0 g Trans Fat, 50 mg Chol, 310 mg Sod, 3 g Carb, 0 g Fib, 27 g Prot, 4% Calc. **POINTS** value: 4.

try it Use leftover vinaigrette for salad dressing (serve tuna over a bed of mixed greens), or as a tasty, Asian-inspired marinade for chicken breast or pork tenderloin.

ASIAN PORK AND VEGETABLE STIR-FRY

½ cup uncooked instant brown rice

1 cup water

1 (¼-pound) boneless pork loin chop, cut into thin bite-size strips

2 cups fresh mushrooms, sliced

1 medium onion, cut in thin wedges

½ teaspoon garlic powder

1 can (18.5-ounce) Progresso° Light Homestyle Vegetable and Rice Soup

1 tablespoon stir-fry sauce

1 cup fresh snow pea pods

2 tablespoons sliced almonds, if desired

Hands-On Prep 30 minutes

Cook 30 minutes

Serves 2

Makes (1½ cups stir-fry and 1 cup rice)

6 POINTS VALUE

1 In 1-quart saucepan, cook rice in water as directed on package, omitting butter.

2 Meanwhile, in 12-inch nonstick skillet, place pork, mushrooms, and onion; sprinkle with garlic powder. Cook over high heat 4–6 minutes, stirring frequently, until pork begins to brown. Stir in soup and stir-fry sauce; heat to boiling. Stir in pea pods. Cook over high heat 5–7 minutes, stirring occasionally, until pea pods are crisp-tender.

3 Serve pork mixture over rice; sprinkle with almonds.

Per serving (¾ cup stir-fry & ½ cup rice): 320 Cal, 5 g Fat, 1.5 g Sat Fat, 0 g Trans Fat, 35 mg Chol, 1190 mg Sod, 49 g Carb, 8 g Fib, 20 g Prot, 6% Calc. *POINTS* value: **6.**

LEMON-RASPBERRY BREAD PUDDING

4 individual 1-cup oven-safe ramekins

6 Weight Watchers Lemon Cake with Lemon Icing, cut into equal small pieces or 1 (5.7-ounce) box

1 cup fresh raspberries

¾ cup fat-free egg substitute

¾ cup fat-free milk

½ teaspoon cinnamon

½ teaspoon pure vanilla extract

1 teaspoon whole-wheat flour

Hands-On Prep **5 minutes**

Cook **20–25 minutes**

Makes **4 servings**

3 POINTS VALUE

1 Preheat oven to 350°F. Lightly coat each ramekin with nonstick spray.

2 Divide cake pieces evenly among each ramekin. Add equal amounts of raspberries to each ramekin by placing them between cake pieces.

3 In a medium bowl, whisk together egg substitute, milk, cinnamon, vanilla extract, and flour. Pour egg mixture into glass measuring cup; pour even amount of mixture into each ramekin.

4 Place ramekins in the oven and bake until egg mixture is set, 20–25 minutes. Let sit for 5 minutes before serving.

Per serving (1 ramekin): 180 Cal, 4 g Fat, 1.5 g Sat Fat, 0 g Trans Fat, 10 mg Chol, 120 mg Sod, 28 g Carb, 5 g Fib, 8 g Prot, 10% Calc. **POINTS** value: **3.**

good idea Serve with a small side of your favorite Weight Watchers yogurt for a smooth, cooling effect.

DARK CHOCOLATE LATTÉ MILK SHAKES

> **4 Weight Watchers GIANT Latté Bars**
> **4 Weight Watchers GIANT Chocolate Fudge Bars**

1 cup fat-free milk

12 ice cubes

2 bananas

Hands-On Prep 10 minutes

Serves 6

Makes 6 cups

3 POINTS VALUE

1 Remove wooden sticks from all ice-cream bars.

2 Combine all ingredients in a blender and purée on high power until mixture is smooth and creamy, 2–4 minutes. Pour equal amounts into glasses and serve immediately.

Per serving (1 cup): 180 Cal, 1.5 g Fat, 0.5 g Sat Fat, 0 g Trans Fat, 5 mg Chol, 105 mg Sod, 42 g Carb, 7 g Fib, 6 g Prot, 25% Calc. **POINTS** value: **3.**

try it Entertaining during cocktail hour? Give your milk shakes an extra kick by adding a splash of Kahlúa or Godiva, but be sure to factor in the **POINTS** value. Sip and enjoy!

MULTIGRAIN WAFFLE ICE CREAM SANDWICHES

4 multigrain waffles, toasted

> **2 Weight Watchers GIANT Cookies & Cream Bars**

½ cup strawberries, hulled and sliced (divided)

Hands-On Prep 10 minutes

Serves 4 (½ waffle sandwich per serving)

2 POINTS VALUE

Once waffles have cooled to room temperature, place 1 ice cream bar on 1 waffle and remove wooden stick. Using a butter knife, gently spread ice cream evenly across waffle. Arrange ¼ cup strawberries over ice cream, and place 1 waffle on top of strawberries and ice cream to form a sandwich. Repeat with remaining 2 waffles, ice-cream bar, and ¼ cup strawberries. Cut both sandwiches in half and serve immediately.

Per serving (½ sandwich): 150 Cal, 3.5 g Fat, 1 g Sat Fat, 0 g Trans Fat, 0 mg Chol, 270 mg Sod, 29 g Carb, 4 g Fib, 4 g Prot, 6% Calc. **POINTS** value: **2.**

good idea Play around with different flavors for your ice cream sandwiches! Use a variety of Weight Watchers GIANT ice cream bars and pair them with your favorite fruits or berries. For example, try Weight Watchers GIANT Chocolate Fudge Bars with sliced bananas.

blissfulness

Frozen Novelties You're on target. You're making healthy food choices every day. So don't forget about dessert! Whether you're in the mood for something creamy, crunchy, or fruity, treat yourself to a Weight Watchers frozen treat, a great way to satisfy your sweet tooth while on your weight management journey. It's pure decadence in every bite!

With so many delicious varieties and flavors to choose from, you'll always be satisfied:

Ice Cream Bars—all 2 *POINTS* value or less per serving!
Ice Cream Cones—all 2 *POINTS* value or less per serving!
Ice Cream Cups—all 3 *POINTS* value or less per serving!
Ice Cream Sandwiches—all 2 *POINTS* value or less per serving!
Sherbet/Sorbet Bars—all 2 *POINTS* value or less per serving!

TASTY SUGGESTIONS
Enjoy a tasty pick-me-up any time of day. Combine 1 shot of brewed espresso, 1 tablespoon of sugar-free caramel sauce, ¾ cup of fat-free milk, and 1 GIANT Latté Bar in a blender until mixture is smooth. Simply delicious!

CHOCOLATE AMARETTO CHEESECAKE PIE

3 Weight Watchers Double Chocolate Muffins (1 box)

3 tablespoons cold water

1 ½ teaspoons unflavored granulated gelatin

1 (6-ounce) container Weight Watchers Nonfat Amaretto Cheesecake yogurt

1 ½ cups reduced-fat or light whipped topping

1 cup strawberries, hulled and sliced

Hands-On Prep 20 minutes

Chill 60 minutes

Makes 6 servings

1 To make the "pie crust," slice each chocolate muffin into thirds. Line a 9-inch pie plate with muffin slices by pressing down gently and evenly until entire bottom of pie plate is completely covered with muffin slices.

2 Put water in a small microwavable bowl. Sprinkle gelatin on top and let it sit until a sponge is formed, about 2 minutes. Heat in microwave on medium-high power until gelatin melts, about 20 seconds. Stir to ensure gelatin is completely dissolved. If not, continue to microwave 5 seconds at a time until dissolved.

3 Add yogurt to a medium bowl. Stir in gelatin, then gently fold in whipped topping. Spoon mixture onto chocolate-muffin crust and spread evenly across crust to form pie topping. Arrange strawberries in a single layer across pie topping. Refrigerate uncovered for 1 hour before slicing and serving.

Per serving (⅙ of pie): 160 Cal, 4 g Fat, 2.5 g Sat Fat, 0 g Trans Fat, 10 mg Chol, 190 mg Sod, 28 g Carb, 4 g Fib, 3 g Prot, 2% Calc. **POINTS** value: **3.**

good idea For a more decadent treat, combine 2 Weight Watchers Pecan Crowns and 1 tablespoon of fat-free milk in a double-boiler over medium-high heat, stirring constantly until melted. Drizzle dessert sauce over strawberries before refrigerating.

V INDIVIDUAL "TIRAMISU" WITH FRUIT

> **1 Weight Watchers Caramel or Chocolate Cake**

2 tablespoons room-temperature coffee

> **1 teaspoon Weight Watchers Reduced Fat Whipped Cream Cheese Spread**

¼ cup reduced-fat or light whipped topping

½ cup strawberries, hulled and sliced

Hands-On Prep 15 minutes

Serves 1

3 POINTS VALUE

1 Place cake in a small bowl and pour coffee over it. Let coffee absorb for about 5 minutes and cut cake in half.

2 Combine cream cheese and whipped topping in a separate small mixing bowl. Whisk together until well combined and smooth.

3 To layer ingredients, place strawberries in a parfait glass or coffee cup, followed by half a piece of coffee-soaked cake, then half the cream-cheese mixture on top of cake. Repeat with remaining ingredients and continue to layer. Top with a single strawberry slice.

Per serving (1 tiramisu): 160 Cal, 6 g Fat, 3.5 g Sat Fat, 0 g Trans Fat, 10 mg Chol, 15 mg Sod, 28 g Carb, 4 g Fib, 2 g Prot, 2% Calc. *POINTS* value: **3.**

food note Traditional tiramisu (which translates into "carry me up" in Italian) combines sponge cake or ladyfingers, espresso, Marsala wine, and mascarpone (an extra-rich Italian cream cheese), all dusted with grated cocoa. In our guilt-free version, Weight Watchers Reduced Fat Whipped Cream Cheese and reduced-fat whipped topping replace the triple-cream heaviness of mascarpone, and fresh strawberries provide added fiber, antioxidants, and vitamin C.

CONVENIENT

delightfulness

Snack Cakes Who says delicious cakes are off limits? Weight Watchers Snack Cakes are an excellent choice for dessert, or any time of day. Treat yourself to four different flavors of individually wrapped snack cakes, all with 0 grams of trans fat.

Enjoy fresh lemon, savory carrot, sweet caramel, and heavenly chocolate anytime, anywhere. Now you can bring your dessert with you, wherever your day brings you! Keep one at your desk at work to quench those midday munchies, or in your car for an on-the-go treat. Each snack cake is under 100 calories—now that's something to cheer about!

Chocolate Cakes, Lemon Cakes, Carrot Cakes, and Caramel Cakes—only 1 *POINTS* value each!

TASTY SUGGESTIONS
Weight Watchers Snack Cakes are a smart choice any time of year. The Lemon Cakes and Caramel Cakes make excellent cool treats when placed in the freezer. Or, warm up the Chocolate Cakes in the microwave, and add a small spoonful of your favorite Weight Watchers Ice Cream or Yogurt for a delicious winter dessert.

GROWN-UP CREAMSICLES
WITH WHITE WINE AND FRESH MINT

> ¼ cup Tropicana Light 'n Healthy Orange
> Juice Beverage

2 tablespoons chardonnay, or similar full-
bodied white wine

2 cups frozen low-fat vanilla yogurt

1 tablespoon fresh mint leaves, finely chopped

1 teaspoon orange zest, grated

thin orange slices

Hands-On Prep 15 minutes

Freeze 5 hours

Serves 4 (¾ cup per serving)

Makes 3 to 3½ cups

3 POINTS VALUE

1 Combine orange juice beverage, wine, and frozen yogurt in a blender or food processor. Pulse on medium speed until ingredients are thoroughly combined.

2 Transfer mixture to an airtight container with lid. Stir in mint and zest, and mix well. Cover and freeze for at least 5 hours. Use ice cream scoop to serve, and garnish with orange slices if desired.

Per serving (1 creamsicle): 120 Cal, 3 g Fat, 2 g Sat Fat, 0 g Trans Fat, 10 mg Chol, 55 mg Sod, 20 g Carb, 0 g Fib, 3 g Prot, 10% Calc. **POINTS** value: **3.**

express lane This low-maintenance yet sophisticated dessert is great for entertaining, and gives an elegant twist to a childhood favorite. Save time by making this recipe the night before your dinner party, and store in freezer until ready to serve.

CARAMEL FONDUE WITH FRESH FRUIT

> **2 (3-ounce) packages Weight Watchers by Whitman's® Caramel Medallions**
>
> ¼ cup fat-free milk, divided
>
> 2 ½ cups mixed sliced fruit (strawberries, banana, apple)

Hands-On Prep 10 minutes
Cook 15 minutes
Serves **5**
Makes ¾ cup fondue

3 POINTS VALUE

1 Fill a medium pot halfway with water. Cover pot with a medium metal bowl that fits snuggly over pot, ensuring that bowl's bottom is not submerged in water. Bring water to a boil over medium-high heat.

2 Add caramels and milk to bowl, stirring to ensure even melting. When caramels are halfway melted, reduce heat to medium and continue stirring. When milk is fully incorporated and caramels are melted, fondue is done. Serve fondue with ½ cup of sliced fruit per person.

Per serving (½ cup fruit and 2½ tablespoons dip): 170 Cal, 8 g Fat, 6 g Sat Fat, 0 g Trans Fat, 5 mg Chol, 25 mg Sod, 26 g Carb, 8 g Fib, 2 g Prot, 6% Calc. **POINTS** value: **3**.

good idea Enjoy this recipe with coffee and tea when entertaining. You can also dip strawberries or dried apricots into fondue and chill fruits in the refrigerator to make delicious caramel-covered fruits.

SMART
sweetness

Chocolate Candies Bring chocolate back into your food choices! Weight Watchers by Whitman's® Chocolates are offered in twelve decadent, mouth-watering flavors, and each is under 60 calories. Who can resist the smooth mint and dark chocolate Mint Patties, or the chewy, milk chocolate–covered Caramel Medallions? The individual servings make it easy to indulge in your favorites while still staying on track.

You can eat them solo or add them to your favorite dessert recipes—just melt some Coconut candy, dip in fresh strawberries, and voilà! Delectable Coconut Chocolate-Covered Strawberries ready for your next party.

Almond Nougat, English Toffee Squares, Coconut, Pecan Crowns, Crispy Butter Cream Caramel, Mint Patties, Peanut Butter Crunch, Dark Chocolate Mousse, Caramel Medallions, and NougieNutty Chews—each piece only 1 ***POINTS*** value! Peanut Butter Cups—each piece only 2 ***POINTS*** value! Caramel Drops—7 pieces only 3 ***POINTS*** value!

TASTY SUGGESTIONS
For a delicious alternative to the Caramel Fondue with Fresh Fruit (page 90), melt the Peanut Butter Cups and serve with slices of fresh apples.

SENSIBLE

tastiness

Cookies Making smart choices doesn't mean sacrificing your favorite tasty treats. So grab a delicious Chocolate Chip or Oatmeal Raisin Cookie and still stay on track!

Weight Watchers Cookies come in two classic flavors, Chocolate Chip and Oatmeal Raisin, and the individually-wrapped portions make it easier than ever to stay on track *and* still indulge your sweet side. Each cookie contains 2.5 grams of fat and is a great source of fiber.

TASTY SUGGESTIONS

Create your own ice cream sandwich! Take a scoop of GIANT Vanilla Fudge Ice Cream (or any of your favorite flavors) and place it between two Oatmeal Raisin Cookies for a deliciously sweet and portable treat.

Each Chocolate Chip and Oatmeal Raisin Cookies has a *POINTS* value of one!

INDEX

A

Amaretto Chocolate
Cheesecake Pie, 84, *85*
Apple Napoleon, 34, *35*
Asian Pork and Vegetable Stir-
Fry, 78

B

Baked Blueberry-Peach French
Toast, 19
Banana-Orange Yogurt Chiller, 20
Beans, Black, Veggie Burrito
with Avocado Salsa and, 58
Beef and Vegetable Stroganoff-
Topped Potato, 60
Blueberry Muffin, Toasted, with
Warm Citrus Compote, 14
Blueberry-Peach French Toast,
Baked, 19
Blue Cheese, Pasta Salad with
Walnuts, Arugula, and, 75
Blue Cheese-Spinach Dip,
Vegetable Kabobs with, 36
Bread Pudding, Lemon-
Raspberry, 79
Breakfast Pizza with Turkey
Sausage, 26
Breakfast Veggie Casserole,
24, *25*
Burrito, Veggie, with Black
Beans and Avocado Salsa, 58

C

Caramel Fondue with Fresh
Fruit, 90, *91*
Carrot Soup, Spiced, 62
Casserole, Breakfast Veggie,
24, *25*
Cheesecake Pie, Chocolate
Amaretto, 84, *85*
Chicken:
    and Chile Wraps, 39
    Curry Salad, 38
    Fingers, with Ranch Dip
    and Seasoned Fries, 64
    Stir-Fried, Broccoli, Red
    Peppers, and Cashews, 65
Chickpea Dip, Lemon-Mint,
with Pita Chips, 72
Chile and Chicken Wraps, 39
Chilled Fruit Soup To-Go with
Yogurt, 30, *31*
Chocolate Amaretto
Cheesecake Pie, 84, *85*
Chocolate Latte Milk Shakes,
Dark, 80, *81*
Chocolate Muffins, Warm, with
Baked Peaches and Sour
Cream, 16, *17*

Cod, Pan-Roasted, with Orange
"Beurre Blanc," 67
Cornmeal Pancakes with Fruity
Yogurt Sauce, 18
Creamsicles with White Wine
and Fresh Mint, 89
Curry Chicken Salad, 38

D

Dark Chocolate Latte Milk
Shakes, 80, *81*
Dip:
    Lemon-Mint Chickpea, with
    Pita Chips, 72
    Ranch, Chicken Fingers
    with Seasoned Fries
    and, 64
    Spinach-Blue Cheese,
    Vegetable Kabobs with, 36

E

Edamame Spread, Lean Ham
Sandwich with, 42, *43*
Eggplant-Mozzarella Panini
with Sun-Dried Tomato
Spread, 46
Eggs Florentine, 22, *23*
Endive Spears with Smoked
Trout and Chive Cream
Cheese, 73
English Muffin, Hot Tuna Melt
on, 52

F

Fig Spread, Make-Ahead
Breakfast, 10, *11*
Fish:
    Cod, Pan-Roasted, with
    Orange "Beurre Blanc," 67
    Salmon, Pan-Seared, with
    Basil-Dijon Cream Sauce,
    68, *69*
    Salmon, Smoked, and
    Dill Cream Cheese Bagel
    Spread, 12, *13*
    Trout, Smoked, Endive
    Spears with Chive Cream
    Cheese and, 73
    Tuna, Seared, with Soy-
    Citrus Vinaigrette, 76
    Tuna Melt, Hot, on English
    Muffin, 52
Fondue, Caramel, with Fresh
Fruit, 90, *91*
French Toast, Baked Blueberry-
Peach, 19
Frittatas, Individual Ham,
Cheese, and Veggie, 27
Fruit. See also specific types
of fruit

Fresh, Caramel Fondue
with, 90, *91*
Individual "Tiramisu" with,
86, *87*
Soup To-Go, Chilled, with
Yogurt, 30, *31*

G

Goat Cheese, Lentil Salad with
Fresh Mint and, 37
Grilled Pizza with Chicken
Sausage, Onions, and Sweet
Peppers, 59
Grilled Veggie Pocket with
Fresh Herb Pesto, 44
Grown-Up Creamsicles with
White Wine and Fresh Mint, 89

H

Ham, Cheese, and Veggie
Frittatas, Individual, 27
Ham Sandwich, Lean, with
Edamame Spread, 42, *43*
Home-Style Turkey Meatloaf, 66
Hot Tuna Melt on English
Muffin, 52

I

Ice-Cream Sandwiches,
Multigrain Waffle, 82
Individual Ham, Cheese, and
Veggie Frittatas, 27
Individual "Tiramisu" with
Fruit, 86, *87*
Italian-Style Veggie Risotto, 74

K

Kabobs, Vegetable, with
Spinach-Blue Cheese Dip, 36

L

Lamb Gyro with Cucumber Dill
Sauce, 56, *57*
Lean Ham Sandwich with
Edamame Spread, 42, *43*
Lemon-Mint Chickpea Dip with
Pita Chips, 72
Lemon-Raspberry Bread
Pudding, 79
Lentil Salad with Fresh Mint
and Goat Cheese, 37

M

Mac 'N' Cheese, 63
Make-Ahead Breakfast Fig
Spread, 10, *11*
Mango Pudding, 33
Measurement equivalents, 93
Meatloaf, Home-Style Turkey, 66
Milk Shakes, Dark Chocolate
Latte, 80, *81*

Mozzarella-Eggplant Panini
with Sun-Dried Tomato
Spread, 46
Muffins, 15
Toasted Blueberry, with
Warm Citrus Compote, 14
Warm Chocolate, with
Baked Peaches and Sour
Cream, 16, *17*
Multigrain Waffle Ice-Cream
Sandwiches, 82

N

Napoleon, Sliced Apple, 34, *35*

O

Orange-Banana Yogurt Chiller, 20

P

Pancakes, Cornmeal, with
Fruity Yogurt Sauce, 18
Panini, Mozzarella-Eggplant,
with Sun-Dried Tomato
Spread, 46
Pan-Roasted Cod with Orange
"Beurre Blanc," 67
Pan-Seared Salmon with Basil-
Dijon Cream Sauce, 68, *69*
Panzanella Salad, Summertime,
50, *51*
Pasta Salad with Blue Cheese,
Walnuts, and Arugula, 75
Peach-Blueberry French Toast,
Baked, 19
Peppers:
Red, Stir-Fried Chicken
with Broccoli, Cashews
and, 65
Sweet, Grilled Pizza with
Chicken Sausage, Onions,
and, 59
Pesto, Fresh Herb, Grilled
Veggie Pocket with, 44
Pita Chips, Lemon-Mint
Chickpea Dip with, 72
Pita pockets:
Grilled Veggie, with Fresh
Herb Pesto, 44
Lamb Gyro with Cucumber
Dill Sauce, 56, 57
Pizza:
Breakfast, with Turkey
Sausage, 26
Grilled, with Chicken
Sausage, Onions, and
Sweet Peppers, 59
Pork and Vegetable Stir-Fry,
Asian, 78
Potato:
Beef and Vegetable
Stroganoff-Topped, 60
Frittatas, Individual Ham,
Cheese, and Veggie, 27

Seasoned Fries, Chicken
Fingers with Ranch Dip
and, 64
Pudding:
Bread, Lemon-Raspberry, 79
Mango, 33

R

Ranch Dip, Chicken Fingers
with Seasoned Fries and, 64
Raspberry-Lemon Bread
Pudding, 79
Reuben Sandwich, 54, *55*
Risotto, Italian-Style Veggie, 74

S

Salad:
Curry Chicken, 38
Lentil, with Fresh Mint and
Goat Cheese, 37
Pasta, with Blue Cheese,
Walnuts, and Arugula, 75
Summertime Panzanella,
50, *51*
Salmon:
Pan Seared, with Basil-
Dijon Cream Sauce, 68, *69*
Smoked, and Dill Cream
Cheese Bagel Spread, 12, *13*
Sandwich:
Lean Ham, with Edamame
Spread, 42, *43*
Mozzarella-Eggplant Panini,
with Sun-Dried Tomato
Spread, 46
Reuben, 54, *55*
Turkey Bagel-, with
Avocado and Green Apple,
40, *41*
Sausage:
Chicken, Grilled Pizza with
Onions, Sweet Peppers,
and, 59
Turkey, Breakfast Pizza
with, 26
Seared Tuna with Soy-Citrus
Vinaigrette, 76, *77*
Sliced Apple Napoleon, 34, *35*
Smoked Salmon and Dill Cream
Cheese Bagel Spread, 12, *13*
Snack Mix, Teriyaki, 47
Soup:
Chilled Fruit To-Go, with
Yogurt, 30, *31*
Spiced Carrot, 62
Spiced Carrot Soup, 62
Stir-Fried Chicken with
Broccoli, Red Peppers, and
Cashews, 65
Stroganoff-Topped Potato,
Vegetable and Beef, 60
Summertime Panzanella Salad,
50, *51*

Sun-Dried Tomato Spread,
Eggplant-Mozzarella Panini
with, 46

T

Teriyaki Snack Mix, 47
"Tiramisu" with Fruit,
Individual, 86, *87*
Toasted Blueberry Muffin with
Warm Citrus Compote, 14
Trout, Smoked, Endive Spears
with Chive Cream Cheese
and, 73
Tuna, Seared, with Soy-Citrus
Vinaigrette, 76
Tuna Melt, Hot, on English
Muffin, 52
Turkey:
Bagel-Sandwich with
Avocado and Green Apple,
40, *41*
Meatloaf, Home-Style, 66
Sausage, Breakfast Pizza
with, 26

V

Vegetable:
and Beef Stroganoff-Topped
Potato, 60
Kabobs, with Spinach-Blue
Cheese Dip, 36
Stir-Fry, Asian Pork and, 78
Veggie:
Breakfast Casserole, 24, *25*
Burrito, with Black Beans
and Avocado Salsa, 68
Frittatas, Individual Ham,
Cheese and, 27
Pocket, with Fresh Herb
Pesto, 44
Risotto, Italian-Style, 74

W

Waffle Ice-Cream Sandwiches,
Multigrain, 82
Warm Chocolate Muffins with
Baked Peaches and Sour
Cream, 16, *17*
White Wine and Fresh Mint,
Grown-Up Creamsicles with, 89
Wraps, Chicken and Chile, 39

Y

Yogurt:
Chilled Fruit Soup To-Go
with, 30, *31*
Chiller, Orange-Banana, 20
Sauce, Fruity, Cornmeal
Pancakes with, 18

RECIPES BY *POINTS*® VALUE

1 *POINTS* VALUE

Caramel Medallions, 92
Endive Spears with
Smoked Trout and Chive
Cream Cheese, 73
Make-Ahead Breakfast Fig
Spread, 10
Vegetable Kabobs with
Spinach-Blue Cheese
Dip, 36

2 *POINTS* VALUE

Bagel Spread with Smoked
Salmon and Dill Cream
Cheese, 12
Chilled Fruit Soup-to-Go
with Yogurt, 30
Eggs Florentine, 22
Individual Ham, Cheese,
and Veggie Frittata, 27
Lemon-Mint Chickpea Dip
with Pita Chips, 72
Mango Pudding, 33
Multigrain Waffle Ice-
Cream Sandwiches, 82
Orange-Banana Yogurt
Chiller, 20
Spiced Carrot Soup, 62
Toasted Blueberry Muffin
with Warm Citrus
Compote, 14

3 *POINTS* VALUE

Baked Blueberry-Peach
French Toast, 19
Breakfast Veggie Casserole,
24
Caramel Fondue with Fresh
Fruit, 90
Chocolate Amaretto
Cheesecake Pie, 84
Dark Chocolate Latte
Milkshakes, 80

Grown-Up Creamsicles
with White Wine and
Fresh Mint, 89
Home-Style Turkey
Meatloaf, 66
Individual "Tiramisu" with
Fruit, 86
Italian-Style Veggie
Risotto, 74
Lemon-Raspberry Bread
Pudding, 79
Lentil Salad with Fresh
Mint and Goat Cheese, 37
Pan-Roasted Cod with
Orange "Beurre Blanc",
67
Warm Chocolate Muffins
with Baked Peaches and
Sour Cream, 16

4 *POINTS* VALUE

Cornmeal Pancakes with
Fruity Yogurt Sauce, 18
Curry Chicken Salad, 38
Lean Ham Sandwich with
Edamame Spread, 42
Seared Tuna with Soy-
Citrus Vinaigrette, 76
Sliced Apple Napolean, 34
Summertime Panzanella
Salad, 50
Teriyaki Snack Mix, 47

5 *POINTS* VALUE

Breakfast Pizza with
Turkey Sausage, 26
Eggplant-Mozzarella
Panini with Sun-Dried
Tomato Spread, 46
Grilled Veggie Pocket with
Fresh Herb Pesto, 44
Hot Tuna Melt on English
Muffin, 52

Pasta Salad with Blue
Cheese, Walnuts, and
Arugula, 75
Reuben Sandwich, 54
Stir-Fried Chicken with
Broccoli, Red Peppers,
and Cashews, 65

6 *POINTS* VALUE

Asian Pork and Vegetable
Stir-Fry, 78
Grilled Pizza with Chicken
Sausage, Onions, and
Sweet Peppers, 59
Lamb Gyro with Cucumber
Dill Sauce, 56
Mac 'n' Cheese, 63

7 *POINTS* VALUE

Beef and Vegetable
Stroganoff-Topped
Potato, 60
Chicken Fingers with
Ranch Dip and Seasoned
Fries, 64
Pan-Seared Salmon with
Basil-Dijon Cream Sauce,
68
Turkey Bagel-Sandwich
with Avocado and Green
Apple, 40

8 *POINTS* VALUE

Chicken and Chile Wraps,
39

10 *POINTS* VALUE

Veggie Burrito with Black
Beans and Avocado
Salsa, 58